GRADED SELECTIONS

FOR

INFORMAL READING DIAGNOSIS

GRADED SELECTIONS

FOR

INFORMAL READING DIAGNOSIS

Grades 4 Through 6

NILA BANTON SMITH

Professor of Education
New York University

with the assistance of

ANNA HARRIS

School Psychologist
Mount Vernon, New York

NEW YORK UNIVERSITY PRESS

SECOND PRINTING 1969

© 1963 BY NEW YORK UNIVERSITY

LIBRARY OF CONGRESS CATALOG CARD NUMBER: 63–11299

MANUFACTURED IN THE UNITED STATES OF AMERICA

ACKNOWLEDGMENT

Grateful acknowledgment is made to Silver Burdett Company, Morristown, New Jersey, for permission to reprint the stories in this book. These stories are taken from fourth, fifth, and sixth grade readers by Nila Banton Smith and Stephen F. Bayne. The titles of the readers are *Distant Doorways, Frontiers Old and New* and *On the Long Road,* respectively. The pictures are photographic reproductions of those that appear in the readers, most of which are in color in the original books.

THE PURPOSE OF THIS BOOK

This book was prepared for use in making a functional inventory: (1) of a pupil's instructional level in reading; and (2) of his skills in literal comprehension, in interpretation, and in word recognition.

Classroom teachers and reading clinicians have found that a functional inventory making use of graded reading textbooks is the most effective means of ascertaining a pupil's instructional level. Although standardized reading tests have many valuable uses, rarely do their results pinpoint the grade level at which corrective or remedial instruction should begin.

Betts's report of a study he made in regard to this matter contains the following statement:

> In a recent study by the Reading Clinic staff, it was found that not one of several standardized reading tests designed for use at fifth-grade level was adequate for determining the achievement levels of pupils at upper and lower ends of the distribution. Although ten percent of the class did not exhibit desirable reading behavior on first-grade materials, some of these tests graded these pupils no lower than second-, third- or fourth-grade level. In general, standardized tests may be expected to rate pupils from one to four grades above their manifest achievement levels. This is a caution to people

who attempt to use standardized test data as a sole criterion for appraising achievement level.[1]

Standardized tests *do* have their uses. Among their valuable uses the following might be mentioned: to identify students who are above or below the norm for their grade; to compare the achievement of students over a given period; to compare the norms of a school or school system with national norms. Every classroom teacher and reading clinician should make use of standardized tests, especially for the purpose of having a scientific basis for comparing scores before and after instruction to appraise the amount of growth made. But when the teacher or clinician wishes to find out whether to start instruction with a pupil at first grade, third grade, fifth grade, or some other level, then functional testing with graded reading textbooks seems to be the most effective measure to use. This functional testing is simply a matter of "trying on" reading content at different levels of difficulty until the one is found that best "fits" the individual being considered. But of course checks must be made of comprehension, interpretation, and word recognition in order to find out which grade-level book *does* "fit" the best. Many reading teachers throughout the country are using the functional inventory procedures in deciding upon the instructional level of pupils in developmental reading classes and of pupils who are about to begin corrective or remedial work. In order to make a functional diagnosis, it is necessary to have carefully graded reading material at hand. Ordinarily, in doing functional testing, teachers must supply themselves with a large number of readers representing several different grade levels. Furthermore, usually no questions are provided with the selections for the purpose of checking literal comprehension or interpretation of reading for diagnostic purposes. The vocabulary for the stories read is not organized for the purpose of aiding teachers to diagnose specific word recognition difficulties. The teacher must prepare such materials in connection with the stories for diag-

[1] Emmett A. Betts, *Foundations of Reading Instruction* (New York: American Book Company, 1957), p. 441.

nostic use or else make a guess concerning the pupil's instructional level as a result of general impressions gathered while he is reading.

The first handbook in this series, covering first-, second-, and third-grade levels, has proved to be of great value both to classroom teachers and to reading clinicians. This second handbook in the series extends the materials to cover fourth-, fifth-, and sixth-grade levels. In addition to the reading selections themselves, this book includes the following: (1) a set of "Literal Comprehension Questions" based on each selection, (2) a set of "Interpretation Questions" based on each selection, (3) lists of words that appear within each selection, organized in groups representing various phonic and word structure elements so that the teacher may locate the words a child misses within certain groups and thus ascertain the types of elements on which the child needs special practice.

HOW TO USE THIS MATERIAL

IN FUNCTIONAL TESTING

Scope of the Material

The selections included in this book represent easy and difficult material found in each of the reading texts in a basal series of readers, grades four through six respectively. Since there is a progression in difficulty within each of these books, one selection was chosen from the early part of each book, and another selection from the latter part of the same book. Thus there are two levels of difficulty represented for each grade; for example, there is an easy and a more difficult selection from the fourth reader; an easy and a more difficult selection from the fifth reader, and similarly, an easy and a more difficult selection from the sixth reader.

Administering a Functional Reading Test

The first step in using this material for functional diagnosis is to select a story that is several grade levels lower than the pupil's expectancy level in reading. Possibly you will find it necessary to start with *Graded Selections for Informal Reading Diagnosis, Grades One through Three.*

Have the pupil read the story to you orally. As he reads check each word that he does not pronounce correctly in one of the lists of words in the "Checking Aids for Teachers" which accompanies the story, or write it on a separate piece of paper.

Also, indicate the mispronunciation of each word he attempts to pronounce. Most teachers do not care to place checkmarks in the book itself, so they write the words on a piece of paper as the pupil misses them, and then later rearrange the words according to the headings given in the "Checking Aids." The pupil should be permitted to go on with his reading without correction or interruption when he mispronounces a word. If the unrecognized word holds him up unduly, tell it to him and let him go on with his reading. In any case you will of course record the word missed, unless it is one of the Mexican words noted on pages 58 and 113, or the proper name *Shawondasee* noted on page 19. In these cases the word should not be included in the list of words missed because it is not a representative sample.

Diagnosing Comprehension

When a pupil has finished reading the selection, ask him to answer the "Comprehension Questions" that follow the story. These questions are not to be read by the pupil. They are to be asked by the teacher. If the sense of an answer is correct, the pupil should be given credit even though the wording is not exactly the same as the answer given in this book. Allow a score of 10 for each correct answer when there are 10 questions asked, and a score of 20 for each correct answer when 5 questions are asked.

Proceed to have the "Interpretation Questions" answered in the same way. Allow a score of 10 for each correct answer when there are 10 questions asked, and a score of 20 for the correct answer when 5 questions are asked. Interpretation questions do not always lend themselves to one specific answer, so in some cases alternative answers are given in this book, any one of which may be considered correct. Other variations may be accepted if they give evidence of good thinking.

Some stories at the middle-grade level are quite long. In such cases "Literal Comprehension Questions" and "Interpretation Questions" are provided in groups of 10, or in some cases 5,

x

for each of several different parts of the story. If you think that it is not necessary to have a pupil read one of these longer stories all the way through, you may have him stop at the end of Part I or Part II, and for each part you will still have available 10, or in some cases 5, questions of each type which you may use for testing purposes.

In case you have a pupil read all parts of a long story, then find the average score which he made on the "Literal Comprehension Questions" for all parts, and similarly the average score for "Interpretation Questions" on all parts. The average score in each case should stand for the score he earned in reading the entire story.

The "Interpretation Questions" are usually much more difficult for children to answer than the "Literal Comprehension Questions." A child may make an excellent score on the "Literal Comprehension Questions" and a very low score on the "Interpretation Questions." Such a situation usually indicates a need for much more guidance in learning to *think* about meanings in reading, and in gathering and supplying meanings not stated directly in the sentences themselves.

If a pupil makes scores lower than those indicated in the table below, both in literal comprehension and interpretation as well as in word recognition, then the material is evidently too difficult for him. If his word recognition score is high in relation to his scores in both types of comprehension, then he should be given special practice in reading for meanings of both types.

Diagnosing Word Recognition Difficulties

Having the pupil attempt to pronounce a list of isolated words is no guarantee that he will or will not be able to recognize the words when he meets them in context. Similarly, having the pupil give an audible sound for isolated letters or combinations of letters is no guarantee that he will apply phonics effectively in pronouncing an unrecognized word in context. The most reliable test of a child's word recognition ability is a functional test in which he has an opportunity to pronounce words embedded in printed sentences and to use word-attack procedures in "figuring out" unrecognized words as he meets such words while actually reading the printed page.

The words the pupil fails to recognize when reading can provide valuable clues to his word recognition needs. If all words missed are checked or grouped under the headings appearing in the section on "Checking Aids for Teachers," you will very frequently find that the words missed fall under the same categories. This indicates that the pupil needs help in those particular areas. As an example, suppose that a pupil repeatedly missed *black, clean, flew, please, close,* and *flat.* This might indicate that he needed help on the blends in which a consonant is combined with *l.* Suppose he repeatedly missed *car, hard, burn, bird,* and *for.* Perhaps in this case he needs instruction in regard to the sounds of vowels followed by *r.* Suppose further, that he repeatedly dropped the endings in *flowers, filled, calling,* and *loudly.* Then it is evident that he needs help in recognizing and pronouncing inflectional endings.

In order to aid the teacher in locating specific areas in which a pupil is having difficulty, words from each story are arranged under the headings: Initial Consonants, Final Consonants, Consonants with Two or More Sounds, Initial Blends, Medial Blends, Final Blends, Initial Speech Sounds, Medial Speech Sounds, Final Speech Sounds, Vowel Sounds, Compound Words, Hyphenated Words, Inflectional Endings,[2] Prefixes, Suffixes, Contractions, and Possessives. If several words are repeatedly missed in one or more of these categories, then the pupil needs special word recognition instruction in these particular areas. Further, a study of the words missed in terms of the headings under which they are organized may indicate the *particular word elements* on which the pupil needs practice.

If a detailed word recognition diagnosis is desired, it is advis-

---

[2] The inflectional endings *s, es, ed, ing, er,* and *est* might also be included under the classification of Suffixes. These inflectional endings occur more frequently and are usually less difficult for children than other suffixes, so for diagnostic purposes they are placed in a group by themselves under "Checking Aids for Teachers" in this book.

able to have the pupil read entire stories while you check or write the words missed. Some indication of word recognition difficulties may be obtained, however, even in reading a part of each of several different stories, if you record the words missed and then organize these words into categories as given in the lists following each story in this book.

In the "Checking Aids for Teachers" you will find a statement of the number of words in a short story, or the number in each part of a long story. These word counts are provided primarily for the teacher's use in computing word recognition scores.

In computing the word recognition score, divide the number of words missed by the entire number of words read to arrive at a percentage score. As an example of this procedure: Part I of *Jack and June in Congoland* contains 246 words. If a child missed 22 words in this part of the story, his percentage score in word recognition could be found as follows: Divide 22 by 246, yielding 8.9% as the percentage of words missed; subtract 8.9% from 100%, leaving 91.06% as the percentage of words recognized. This would be the pupil's score in word recognition for Part I of the story.

Finding a Pupil's Instructional Level

Have the pupil read selections of increasing difficulty until you find his instructional level. This is the level that is easy enough so that he can read with enjoyment and will not experience discouragement, but which at the same time will be sufficiently difficult so that learning elements can be pulled out for instructional purposes. The instructional level is usually the grade level at which the pupil makes scores approximating the following:

Comprehension	85% to 90%
Interpretation	70% to 75%
Pronunciation	95%

Checking Rate of Silent Reading

Ordinarily rate is not given consideration in finding a pupil's instructional level. If, however, the teacher wishes to ascertain the rate of some of her pupils in their silent reading of narrative material at their respective instructional levels, the selections in this book can be used for this purpose.

An informal procedure for obtaining a check on reading rate is as follows: Get a stopwatch or watch with a second hand. Have the pupil find the selection which you wish to use for checking purposes. (Perhaps you will wish to use only a part of a selection; if so choose a part that has 400 or more words in it.) Ask the pupil to put his finger in the book to keep the place, then close the book. Look at your watch, and when the second hand is at 6 or 12, tell the pupil to open the book and start reading silently, and to look up at you when he has finished reading. Jot down the time that it took the pupil to read the selection in minutes and seconds; for example, 3 minutes, 40 seconds. Reduce this total time to seconds—$3 \times 60 + 40 = 220$ seconds. Refer to the "Checking Aids for Teachers" to find the number of words in the story or part of the story read. Divide the total number of words read by the total number of seconds and multiply by 60 to get the number of words per minute covered in the reading. As an example: If the pupil read Part I of "Lupe's Wish," which contains 631 words, in the 220 seconds indicated above, the number of words per minute which he read could be derived as follows:

$$\frac{631}{220} \times 60 = 168 \text{ WPM}$$

The pupil should always be checked both for literal comprehension and interpretation following an informal check of his rate as indicated above. Comprehension and speed should always progress in relation to one another.

TABLE OF CONTENTS

GRADED SELECTIONS

FOR

INFORMAL READING DIAGNOSIS

JACK AND JUNE IN CONGOLAND

A Little Jungle Friend

At last Jack and June were really in Congoland. They had traveled up the great Congo River with Father and Mother to one of the jungle towns. Now they were going to live at the hotel in the town while Father took a trip into the jungle. He was going to take pictures of pygmies.

Pygmies are small people. The men and women are not even five feet tall. Jack and June wanted very much to go with Father to visit these shy little people. But Father had said that the trip to the pygmies' camps in the jungle would be too long and too hot for the children.

After Father left to take pictures of the pygmies, Jack and June met Alber. He was a little Congo boy who lived in the town. He could speak the English language. He knew the ways of the jungle animals. In the jungle along the river Alber showed Jack many interesting things.

One day the boys were watching a family of wild monkeys at play in the trees.

"June would like one of those little monkeys for a pet," said Jack.

1

"Wild monkeys do not make good playmates. They would rather play with each other in the jungle," said Alber. "But June may play with my pet monkey some day soon.

"Now I want to show you the place where my father killed a leopard with a poisoned arrow. It is on the way to the elephant trap."

Drums of the Congo

That night Jack told his mother and June what Alber had shown him in the jungle. He told them about the leopard Alber's father had killed and about the wonderful trap for elephants. As the children and their mother talked, they could hear the high, sharp sounds of Congo horns and bells above the noise of drums.

2

"Alber and his people are dancing and singing in their part of the town," said Mother.

"Maybe Alber will tell us something about Congo music tomorrow," said June.

The next day Alber brought Jack a little drum. It was made of a coconut shell and a piece of skin. He also brought June a tiny drum which the pygmies used.

Alber showed the children how to beat the drums with their hands. Jack and June had great fun beating their drums.

Then Alber took Mother and the children to a place just outside the town. Here they saw a talking drum. It was a big tree trunk that had been hollowed out. When the drummer beat the hollow log with two heavy sticks, it made a noise that could be heard for many miles.

"The drummers can make these drums say many different things when they beat them," said Alber. "That is the way messages are sent. These messages can be heard far away in the jungle."

Jack and June wanted to stay for a long time and watch the drummer. But after they had watched him for a little while, Mother said it was time to go back to the hotel for lunch.

Before Alber left them to go to his home, he told Jack and June that he would bring them a surprise very soon.

Alber's Surprise

Later that day Alber brought his pet monkey to the hotel. When June saw it, she said, "A little monkey is just what I have been wanting."

"I'll come for her tonight," said Alber. "If she is bad, you must tell me."

June had great fun dressing the monkey in doll's clothes. Then the children took the monkey for a walk. Each child held one of the monkey's little hands as she skipped along between them.

That night, when Alber came for his monkey, June said, "She has been a very good playmate. I hope you will bring her again tomorrow."

"She is not always good," laughed Alber. "But I'll bring her again tomorrow."

The next afternoon, while Jack and June stayed in the hotel, Mother went to visit some

4

friends. Alber brought the monkey again and left her to play with the children.

"Today I am going to put my doll's hat and coat on the monkey," said June. "Then we can go to meet Mother."

June put the hat and the little coat on the monkey. Suddenly the monkey jumped away from June and ran across the bed to a window. The window blind, made of palm-leaf stems, was partly open. The monkey climbed to the top of the blind. There she sat chattering as if she were in the jungle.

"Come down! Come down!" begged June. "Please be a good monkey and come down!"

But the monkey would not come down. Back and forth, back and forth, she walked, making funny faces and chattering loudly.

"What shall we do, Jack? How can we catch her?" cried June.

"We must call Alber," said Jack. "He will know how to catch his pet monkey."

The children ran out to find Alber. After they found him, the three of them came back to the hotel. The monkey was sitting in front of a looking glass. She had opened Mother's box of powder.

5

There was powder on the monkey's hands and face, and also a great deal of powder on the floor. When the monkey saw the children, she climbed quickly up the window blind again.

All the children began to laugh when they saw the monkey's white face and hands. Alber put his hand in his pocket and took out some peanuts. "Come down, and I'll give you these peanuts," he said.

The monkey climbed part way down the window blind and reached for the peanuts. At that moment Alber caught her by the neck.

Alber scolded her. "You are a bad little monkey," he said. "June will never want you to come again."

The monkey hid her powdered face in her little hands.

"She is sorry about spilling the powder," said Jack.

"Even if she did spill the powder," said June, "she is a good playmate."

CHECKING AIDS FOR TEACHERS

LEVEL: Fourth Reader, early part of book

Jack and June in Congoland

COMPREHENSION CHECKS

Part I   A Little Jungle Friend
Pages 1–2, 246 words

LITERAL COMPREHENSION QUESTIONS

1   What was the name of the river on which Jack and June traveled?
ANSWER: The Congo River.

2   Where were the mother and two children going to live?
ANSWER: They were going to live in a hotel.

3   What was Father going to do in the jungle?
ANSWER: He was going to take pictures of the pygmies.

4   How tall are the pygmies?
ANSWER: They are less than five feet tall.

5   Who was Alber?
ANSWER: A little Congo boy who lived in the town.

6   What language could Alber speak in addition to his own language?

ANSWER: He could speak the English language.

7 What were some of the things Alber knew?

ANSWER: He knew the ways of jungle animals; he knew where there were interesting things along the river.

8 What did Jack think June might like to have?

ANSWER: A wild monkey for a pet.

9 What animal did Alber's father kill?

ANSWER: A leopard.

10 With what did he kill the leopard?

ANSWER: A poisoned arrow.

INTERPRETATION QUESTIONS

1 Why would the Congo or any other river be called "a great river"?

ANSWER: Because it is a large river—both wide and long.

2 Why didn't Father live at the hotel with the rest of the family?

ANSWER: Because it would take too much time to go back and forth from the town into the jungle.

3 Why didn't Father take the children into the jungle?

ANSWER: It might have been dangerous, or too hot.

4 Why do you think it might be difficult for Father to take pictures of the pygmies?

ANSWER: Since they were shy people, they might not want to pose, or they might be afraid of the camera.

5 What do you suppose Father was going to do with the pictures?

ANSWER: Maybe he was going to use them in a movie or a TV program, or publish them in a magazine or book, or show them to his friends for their entertainment.

6 How do you think Alber learned the English language?

ANSWER: Probably he learned it from the English traders he met in the town.

7 How do you think Alber's life might have been different from that of Jack and June?

ANSWER: He probably lived in a different kind of house, wore different clothes, ate different food, had different pets, played different games.

8 What activities might be important in the Congo that we would not be familiar with?

ANSWER: Killing animals with bows and arrows; trapping animals.

9 Why don't wild monkeys make good playmates?

ANSWER: They are used to the jungle and do not like to be caged, or they might bite the children.

10 How could an arrow be made poisonous?

ANSWER: Probably by dipping the tip into a poisonous liquid.

Part II   *Drums of the Congo*
Pages 2–4, 284 words

LITERAL COMPREHENSION QUESTIONS

1 About what two things did Jack tell Mother and June that night?

ANSWER: He told them about the leopard Alber's father had killed and about the elephant trap.

2 Name the three musical instruments that Mother and the children heard.

ANSWER: Congo horns, bells, and drums.

3 What were Alber and his people doing?

ANSWER: They were dancing and singing.

4 What did Alber bring Jack the next day?

ANSWER: A tiny drum.

5 Out of what materials was it made?

ANSWER: It was made of a coconut shell and a piece of skin.

6 Where did Mother and the children see the talking drum?

ANSWER: At a place just outside the town.

7 Out of what was the talking drum made?

ANSWER: It was made out of a hollowed-out tree trunk.

8 How far could the talking drum be heard?

ANSWER: It could be heard for many miles.

9 Of what use is the talking drum to the jungle people?

ANSWER: It is used to send messages.

10 What did Alber tell the children before they left for lunch?

ANSWER: He told them he would bring them a surprise.

Interpretation Questions

1 Why was the drum called a talking drum?

ANSWER: Because jungle people sent messages with the use of such a drum.

2 How do you suppose these people made a trap for elephants?

ANSWER: Perhaps they dug a deep hole that the elephants fell into (or any other logical explanation).

3 Why were Alber and his people dancing and singing?

ANSWER: This was one of the ways they had of amusing themselves, or they might have been having a feast or celebrating a successful hunt.

4 How could a drum be made from a piece of coconut shell and a piece of skin?

ANSWER: The coconut shell might be cut into two parts, then a piece of skin might be stretched tightly over the opening to one part and then tied.

5   Compare musical instruments in the Congo with musical instruments in our country.

    ANSWER: They have horns, bells, and drums; we have these instruments and also pianos, violins, flutes, and so on.

6   How do you think the natives hollowed out the big tree trunk?

    ANSWER: They may have burned out the inside of the trunk, or they may have used a chisel or other sharp tools to chip away the inside of the log.

7   How do you think the drummer could make the drum say different things?

    ANSWER: By beating louder or softer on the drum and by changing the rhythm of the beat.

8   How does the use of music by the Congo people differ from our use of music?

    ANSWER: We use music for enjoyment or entertainment by singing it or by listening or dancing to it. The Congo people use music not only for entertainment but as a means of sending messages.

9   Upon what occasions do you think the Congo people sent messages far away in the jungle?

    ANSWER: When in danger of attack by an enemy, or when they wanted other tribes to join them for counsel, or when they wanted to invite others to join them for a celebration or for entertainment.

10 What indications have you that the Congo people were clever?

    ANSWER: They used the things they had on hand to make musical instruments, such as making a drum from a coconut shell and a piece of skin; they found a way to send messages great distances by beating on a hollowed-out tree trunk.

Part III Alber's Surprise
Pages 4–6, 467 words

LITERAL COMPREHENSION QUESTIONS

1 What surprise did Alber have for June?
  ANSWER: He brought his pet monkey.
2 What did the children do with the monkey?
  ANSWER: They dressed it in doll's clothes and took it for a walk.
3 What did Mother do the next afternoon?
  ANSWER: Mother went to visit some friends.
4 What two articles of clothing did June put on the monkey?
  ANSWER: A doll's hat and coat.
5 What three things did the monkey do while she was on the window blind?
  ANSWER: She walked across the blind, made funny faces, and chattered loudly.
6 Why did the children call Alber?
  ANSWER: Because he would know how to catch the monkey.
7 What had the monkey done while the children were calling Alber?
  ANSWER: The monkey had climbed down and opened Mother's box of powder.
8 What had happened to the monkey that made the children laugh?
  ANSWER: The monkey had gotten the white powder over her hands and face.
9 How did Alber catch the monkey?
  ANSWER: Alber offered her some peanuts; when she reached to get them, he caught her.

10 What did the monkey do when Alber scolded her?
ANSWER: She hid her face in her hands.

Interpretation Questions

1 Why did Alber plan to come for the monkey at night?
ANSWER: Since she was a wild monkey, Alber was afraid she might do some damage if she stayed in a house all night.

2 What caused Alber to say, "If she is bad, you must tell me"?
ANSWER: She probably was accustomed to getting into mischief and Alber suspected she might do something she ought not to do.

3 Why can't a wild monkey be considered a good playmate?
ANSWER: One can never tell what it might do. (This monkey climbed up the blind, chattering as if she were in the jungle.)

4 Why did June consider the monkey a good playmate?
ANSWER: Because the monkey let June dress her in doll's clothes and take her for a walk.

5 Why did the monkey climb to the top of the blind?
ANSWER: Because the blind was made of palm-leaf stems and this material was similar to trees and shrubs in the jungle.

6 Why didn't the monkey come down when June called her?
ANSWER: She was having fun; she was showing off.

7 Why did the monkey climb up the window blind again when she saw the children?
ANSWER: She had done a naughty thing and she didn't want to be caught and punished.

13

8 Why did Alber use tricks to catch the monkey?

ANSWER: The monkey would not come down when she was called, so Alber had to think of a way to trick her to make her come down.

9 Why did June seem to forgive the monkey for being so mischievous?

ANSWER: She thought the monkey was sorry about spilling the powder.

10 In what ways did the monkey act like a human being?

ANSWER: She walked with the children; she looked at herself in the mirror; she powdered her face; she hid her face in her hands.

VOCABULARY CHECKS

Organized for Use in Diagnosing Word Recognition Difficulties

As the child reads the story, check any words in these lists which he doesn't recognize. If you don't wish to place check marks in your book, write the words on a separate piece of paper, then later rearrange them according to the headings given in the "Checking Aids." These groupings will indicate on which of the phonic elements or word structure elements the pupil needs special practice.

PHONICS

INITIAL CONSONANTS

back, be, beat, before, bells, boy, box
came, camps, can, come, Congo, could
dancing, day, deal, do
face, family, far, feet, five, for, forth, found, fun
good, go, give

had, hear, heard, hid, high, his, hollow, horn, hotel
jungle, just
killed
language, last, left, leopard, like, live, little, long, lunch
make, many, men, met, miles, moment, monkey, mother
next, noise, not, now
part, people, peanuts, pet, pictures, poisoned, powder, put,
    pygmies
ran, really, reached, river
said, saw, singing, some, soon, sorry, sound, suddenly
take, talked, tall, told, top, tongue, took, town, time
very, visit
watching, way, we, went, were, wild, with, window, women,
    wonderful

FINAL CONSONANTS
music
could, had, heard, good, leopard, said, wild, would
of
big, log
speak, took
hotel, shell, small, tall, tell, will
drum, him, them
been, can, children, even, fun, in, men, shown, skin, soon,
    then, town, women
sharp, up, trap, trip
after, Alber, father, for, floor, hear, later, mother, other,
    powder, rather, river, their
as, glass, his, is, was, us
about, at, beat, brought, but, caught, coconut, different,
    elephant, feet, great, hot, just, last, left, met, moment,
    next, night, not, out, part, pocket, sent, visit, want
box

blind

climbed, clothes

glass

place, play, please

bring, brought

dressing, drums

friend, from, front

great

trap, traveled, tree, trunk

scolded

skin, skipped

small

speak, spill

stayed, sticks

FINAL BLENDS

last

INITIAL SPEECH SOUNDS

chattering, child, children

quickly

shall, sharp, she, showed, shy

that, them, then, there, these, they, those, thing

what, when, where, while, white

MEDIAL SPEECH SOUNDS

quickly

Congo, English, jungle, language

monkey

elephant

father, mother, other, rather

FINAL SPEECH SOUNDS

catch, lunch, much, watch

Jack, stick

along, bring, long, sing

trunk

VOWEL SOUNDS

Long a: came, made, make, place, take

Short a: animals, at, can, family, had, hat, Jack, that, traveled

Long e: even, he, me, these

Short e: bed, elephant, held, left, men, messages, met, next, pet, sent, shell, them, then

16

Long i: blind, five, miles, while, wild

Short i: big, children, hid, his, into, little, killed, live, pictures, river, spill, trip, visit, will, window, with

Long o: coconut, hotel, open, scolded, told, those, window

Short o: box, doll, hot, not, on, pocket

Long u: music, used

Short u: but, drum, fun, jungle, just, lunch, much, must, suddenly, trunk, up

Long y: shy

Short y: sorry

au and aw: caught, saw

ay: away, may, play, stay, ways

ea: beat, each, deal, hear, peanuts, please, reached, really

ea: heavy

ea: great

ee: between, meet, three, tree

ie: cried

ie: piece

oa: coat

oi: noise, poisoned

oo: afternoon, too, soon

oo: good, looking, took

ou: about, found, loudly, outside, sounds

ou: could, would

ou: bought, brought

Vowels followed by r: far, part, sharp, different, interesting, for, forth, horns, surprise

Vowels followed by l or w: all, also, small, talk, tail, saw

Word Variants

COMPOUND WORDS

afternoon, before, coconut, Congoland, maybe, outside, peanuts, playmate, something, tomorrow, tonight, today

17

palm-leaf

INFLECTIONAL ENDINGS
climbed, hollowed, jumped, laughed, lived, poisoned, powdered, scolded, showed, skipped, stayed, traveled, used,
wanted, watched
later, drummer
clothes, messages
beating, chattering, dressing, going, interesting, looking, making, sitting, spilling, talking, wanting, watching
animals, bells, boys, camps, drums, elephants, friends, hands,
horns, miles, monkeys, peanuts, pygmies, stems, sticks,
towns, ways

SUFFIXES
loudly, partly, quickly, really, suddenly
wonderful
funny

POSSESSIVES
Alber's, doll's, monkey's, mother's, pygmies'

CONTRACTIONS
I'll

NOTE

In reading the next story, the proper name *Shawondasee* should not be counted in the list of words which the child misses.

The teacher may help the child to pronounce this word: *Shawondasee* (shä wŭn dā′ sē).

19

THE MAID WITH THE GOLDEN HAIR

Every spring and summer golden-headed dandelions dance among the grasses. Perhaps you have noticed that soon after they have blossomed, their golden heads turn to white fleecy balls. The dandelion seeds are hidden in these soft balls. When the wind blows, the little seeds fly far and wide on their fleecy wings.

Some of the Indians in our country have told their children this charming story of the dandelion.

In the days of long, long ago, Shawondasee, the South Wind, liked to lie idly dreaming under his favorite flowering tree in a meadow. As he slept, he breathed in the sweet perfume of its blossoms. Then he gently breathed the perfume out again, sending it far over the meadow. Soon all the spring air was filled with sweet perfume.

Shawondasee was the most peaceable of the four brother winds. He never blew hard, so he never made trouble for anyone. He was always kind and gentle, but he was lazy and idle too.

One warm spring morning Shawondasee lay

half dreaming under his favorite tree. How happy and peaceful he felt as he breathed in the sweet perfume around him! Just before he fell asleep, he decided to take one more look at the meadow.

Very slowly Shawondasee raised himself and rubbed his eyes. Was he awake or dreaming? A short distance away he saw a beautiful maiden. In the bright morning sun her yellow hair shone like a crown of gold. Shawondasee rubbed his eyes again. No, he was not dreaming. The maiden was really there.

For a long time Shawondasee, the South Wind, lay looking at the beautiful maiden. He wanted to call to her and tell her how beautiful she was.

But as long as he could look at her, he was too lazy and comfortable to call to her. The minutes slipped slowly away. At last darkness came to the meadow, and Shawondasee fell fast asleep. All night he dreamed of the beautiful maiden.

When the sun rose the next morning, Shawondasee raised himself and looked out over the meadow. The maid with the golden hair still stood tall and beautiful against the sun. More than ever Shawondasee wanted to speak to her. But he was too comfortable under his tree to raise his voice or to move. Again the minutes slipped slowly away. Once more darkness came to the meadow.

For several days Shawondasee lay idly under the tree, breathing in its sweet perfume. All day long he rested and looked at the beautiful maiden.

"Soon," he thought to himself, "I shall call to her and tell her how lovely she is."

Then one morning Shawondasee opened one sleepy eye. Alas, he could not see the maiden with the golden hair. He looked around him. Ah! there she was. But how she had changed! Shawondasee sat up and rubbed his eyes. Then he looked again. The maiden's hair no longer shone like gold. Her crown of golden hair was gone. She wore a fleecy white crown instead.

Now he knew what had happened.

"Ah me! Ah me!" sighed Shawondasee. "My brother, the North Wind, has come in the night and put his fleecy crown of silver upon her lovely head. Ah me!" Then with a deep sigh he sank back under his favorite flowering tree.

The sigh was so deep and so long that it floated out over the meadow to the silver-crowned maiden. At once the air was filled with fleecy bits from the silvery crown. On the gentle breath of the South Wind they floated far away.

Then Shawondasee sat up and looked again. He could see nothing. "My brother, the North Wind, has taken the maiden with him," he thought sadly.

Then once more he sank back under his tree and fell fast asleep dreaming of the beautiful maiden.

CHECKING AIDS FOR TEACHERS

LEVEL: Fourth Reader, latter part of book

The Maid with the Golden Hair
Pages 20–23, 637 words

COMPREHENSION CHECKS

LITERAL COMPREHENSION QUESTIONS

1. How are the seeds of the dandelion distributed?
   ANSWER: The wind blows them far and wide.
2. Who told this story to their children?
   ANSWER: Some Indians in our country.
3. What is another name for Shawondasee?
   ANSWER: The South Wind.
4. What did Shawondasee like to do?
   ANSWER: He liked to lie dreaming under a tree in the meadow.
5. Describe Shawondasee.
   ANSWER: He was peaceable; he never blew hard and never made trouble for anyone; he was kind and gentle, but lazy and idle too.
6. What did Shawondasee see when he awoke from his sleep?

ANSWER: He saw a beautiful maiden.

7 Why didn't Shawondasee call to the maiden?
   ANSWER: He was too lazy and comfortable.

8 What change took place in the maiden after several days?
   ANSWER: She had a fleecy white crown instead of golden hair.

9 Who changed the maiden?
   ANSWER: Shawondasee's brother, the North Wind.

10 What happened to the maiden finally?
   ANSWER: The North Wind took her with him.

INTERPRETATION QUESTIONS

1 How do dandelions dance among the grasses?
   ANSWER: When the wind blows, they move or sway back and forth.

2 If Shawondasee had two brothers, in addition to North Wind, what do you think their names might have been?
   ANSWER: East Wind, West Wind.

3 What does the story tell you to prove that Shawondasee was peaceable?
   ANSWER: He never made any trouble.

4 Do you think Shawondasee was awake or dreaming when he saw the maiden? How do you know?
   ANSWER: He was awake. He rubbed his eyes to see if he were dreaming, but he found that he was awake.

5 What proof do you have that the South Wind was lazy?
   ANSWER: He wanted to tell the maiden how beautiful she was, but he never could go to enough effort to call to her.

6 How long do you think Shawondasee rested and slept?

25

ANSWER: Several days, as long as it takes a dandelion to flower and change into ripened seed.

7 Who was the beautiful maiden?

ANSWER: A dandelion.

8 What were the fleecy bits that floated away from the maiden's crown?

ANSWER: They were really dandelion seeds.

9 What do you think happened to the fleecy bits after they were blown away?

ANSWER: They fell to earth, where they probably sprouted and grew the next spring.

10 What were the Indians trying to explain in this story?

ANSWER: The life cycle of a dandelion—flowering, development of seeds, seed dispersal.

VOCABULARY CHECKS

Organized for Use in Diagnosing Word Recognition Difficulties

As the child reads the story, check any words in these lists which he doesn't recognize. If you don't wish to place check marks in your book, write the words on a separate piece of paper, then later rearrange them according to the headings given in the "Checking Aids." These groupings will indicate on which of the phonic elements or word structure elements the pupil needs special practice.

PHONICS

INITIAL CONSONANTS

back, balls, beautiful, before, bits, but

call, comfortable, could, country

dance, dandelions, darkness, days, decided, deep, distance

far, fast, favorite, fell, felt, filled, for, four

hair, half, happened, happy, hard, have, he, heads, hidden, his, how

just
kind
last, lay, lazy, lie, liked, little, long, look, lovely
made, maiden, meadow, minute, more, morning, most, move,
    my
never, next, night, noticed
perfume, peaceful, perhaps, put
raised, really, rested, rose, rubbed
sank, seeds, sending, several, sigh, silver, some, soon, South,
    summer, sun
take, tall, tell, time, to, told, too, turn
very, voice
wanted, warm, was, wide, wind, winds, with, wore

FINAL CONSONANTS
and, around, could, gold, hard, instead, kind, wind
half
look
call, fell, tell
him, warm
crown, dandelion, in, on, soon, sun, then, turn, when, asleep,
    deep
after, air, brother, far, hair, never, our, summer, their, under
always, his, perhaps
but, felt, next, not, sat, short, soft, slept, sweet, that

CONSONANTS WITH TWO SOUNDS
Hard c: call, came, comfortable, country
Soft c: dance, decided, distance, fleecy, noticed, once, peace-
    able, voice
Hard g: again, gold, gone
Soft g: changed, gentle

INITIAL BLENDS
blew, blows, blossomed ·

MEDIAL BLENDS
idle, instead, trouble

27

fleecy, floated, flowering, fly
slept, slipped, slowly
breath, breathed, brother
crown
dreaming
grasses
tree, trouble
still, stood, story
sweet
spring

oa: floated
oi: voice
oo: soon, too
oo: looked
ou: around, out, south
ou: country, trouble
ou: thought
ow: blows, meadow, slowly
ow: crown, how
Vowels followed by r: charming, far, hard, darkness, flowering, her, perfume, never, perhaps, comfortable, favorite, for, short, story, turn, more, wore, before
Vowels followed by l or w: always, ball, call

WORD VARIANTS

COMPOUND WORDS
anyone, himself

HYPHENATED WORDS
golden-headed, silver-crowned

INFLECTIONAL ENDINGS
blossomed, breathed, changed, decided, filled, floated, liked, looked, noticed, opened, rested, rubbed, slipped
longer
grasses
breathing, charming, dreaming, flowering, looking, sending
dandelions, days, heads, minutes, winds, wings

PREFIXES
again, ago, around, asleep, awake, instead

SUFFIXES
comfortable, peaceable, beautiful, peaceful, darkness
lovely, really, slowly
idly, fleecy, silvery
golden, hidden, maiden

POSSESSIVES
maiden's

29

THE BEE TREE

Exploring the Woods

Every morning, when the sun came up, Jane Allen hurried down from her little room under the roof to throw open the door of the cabin. The Allen family had come to America on the *Mayflower*, and they had lived in Plymouth almost two years now. The little village was just two years old. Everybody knew everybody else well, since there were so few people living in the little town at the very edge of this great, new country.

Jane's best friend was Susan Whiting, who lived in the next house down the path. Susan was always up early, too, for the two girls liked to meet for a minute in the morning and tell each other what they were going to do that day. Lately Susan had always said the same thing. "I am going down to the shore to watch for a ship. I want to be the very first one to give the news when a ship from England comes in sight. What are you going to do?"

"I am going to the woods," Jane usually answered. "My mother and I are going to look for wild strawberries." Or sometimes she would say, "My brother Robert is going hunting. He said I could go, too, and carry his powder horn." On this summer morning she said, "Oh, Susan, come with us. The wild raspberries are getting ripe, and the open places in the woods are full of them."

Susan shook her head. "I'm afraid of the woods," she said. "My mother is afraid there, too. We would not go into the woods for anything. Even my father does not like to go hunting as your brother does. He is not used to hunting, and he says there is no telling what he might meet in the woods. We think it is a little strange of you to go to the forest so often and to eat all the queer things that you bring from there. No, I am going to watch for a ship. I am sure there will be one soon now."

When the Pilgrims first came to America, they knew very little about living in a new, wild country. "Bring as much food as you can," their leader had said. "We cannot tell what we will find in America." So they had brought with them, on the *Mayflower*, as much food as the ship would carry. They brought bacon, flour, salt, and sugar. They tried to bring enough food to last them for a long time.

When the Pilgrims landed, they looked at the thick forest which in places came down to the shore, and they began to realize what a great, empty country America was. They were afraid that they would not find enough to eat. "Where will we get flour to make bread?" they asked one another.

Friendly Indians showed them how to plant and to harvest Indian corn. The Pilgrims also learned from the Indians how to grind corn into meal and make it into bread. But it was such strange food!

They saved as much as they could of the flour, salt, and sugar they had brought from England. They used only a little at a time, waiting and waiting for a ship to come from England and bring them more.

A few of the people in Plymouth, like the Allens, believed that in a new country they must learn its ways. Robert Allen had been used to hunting in England. He knew, also, how to fish. So he went hunting and fishing often in the new country, and brought home fresh meat and fish for his mother to cook. Squanto, an Indian who was a good friend of the Pilgrims, taught Robert how to dig clams on the beach, and how to dry the fish that he caught. Therefore at the Allen house there was always plenty of good food—wild turkeys and wild ducks, ground Indian corn, berries and other fruits from the woods.

Today Robert was starting off to hunt partridges. It was a great treat to Jane to go with him. Her strong legs could easily keep up with her brother's fast, long steps. She knew how to step softly when they came in sight of a deer. She was learning from Robert and from Squanto how to make a cry like the call of a wild turkey.

Jane Finds a Bee Tree

Jane ran ahead, for she had seen some flowers with great arrow-shaped heads, bright purple like a king's robe. She ran to pick them, but as she picked the last one, she heard a strange sound. A humming and buzzing was coming from above her head. It was like nothing she had ever heard before. "Come, Robert," she cried. "Quick! Listen. What is that noise?"

Robert caught her arm and pulled her back a little way. "You are under a bee tree," he said. "Hush, and you can hear the bees buzzing inside. See the little holes in the trunk. Look! The bees are going out and in."

As Jane looked up, she saw hundreds of bees

buzzing about the tree. The bark was full of holes; each hole was a door to the hive inside.

"The bees will not sting you," Robert told her, "unless you get in their way. The tree must be full of honey."

Jane stood looking at it, but as Robert walked on she came running after him. He seemed to be thinking about what Mr. Bradford had said, for his face was troubled. At last he said to Jane, "We are having our hardest time. When we have planted corn once more and harvested it, then we will feel safe. We will be sure that we have enough to eat. We all must keep brave hearts until that time. Every person can help. I can help. You can help, too."

When they returned home that evening, Jane's

dress was torn by bushes and twigs, but they had a string of partridges, more than enough for the Allen family. They had, also, a bag of wild plums. When Jane tasted one of them, she made a face, for it was sour indeed. They found Mistress Whiting, Susan's mother, talking to Mistress Allen about the supper for the men on Wednesday.

"It must be a good one," Mistress Allen was saying. "Everybody will feel more hopeful if we show them how much good food there really is in this new country. We must not use up all that we have stored in our cupboards, for that would be wasteful. Robert can get ducks and partridges for us, and all the children can dig clams on the beach."

"But what shall we do for a sweet?" Mistress Whiting was almost crying. "No supper can be called a supper if there is no dessert at the end. I have a big bowl of sugar left. I will gladly give it, though I have saved it for months. What kind of dessert can we make?"

It was then that Jane spoke of her great idea. "We brought home some wild plums today. With plenty of sugar, they could make a good pudding. Mother, do you remember the plum pudding you made last summer?"

Yes, Mistress Allen remembered. "It was not a real plum pudding," she told Mistress Whiting. "A real plum pudding would be too hot and heavy for this summer weather. But it was a good pudding with wild fruit and spices in it. I had not made one this year because we had so little sugar to sweeten it. If you have sugar, we can make a pudding."

Mistress Whiting clapped her hands together. "Now that is the best news I have heard in twelve months. If we can give the men a sweet pudding for their supper, nobody can say that things are so much worse here than they were in England."

The day for the meeting came. The men had begun to gather in the parlor of Mr. Bradford's house, for there was much to talk about, and they had been told to come early. The women had been busy all afternoon in the kitchen. Partridges were roasting, and the clams were all ready to be steamed. There were beans from one garden, lettuce from another. Mistress Whiting and Susan had come together, bringing the bowl of sugar wrapped up in a linen cloth. Mistress Whiting would not let anybody but herself or Susan touch it.

"Open the door into the parlor," she said to Robert. "I want to know how many men are there. We must make ready to mix the pudding."

Jane was behind Robert when he opened the
door. She could see Mr. Bradford sitting by the
fireplace. His face was troubled. One man was
standing by the table, talking. His voice was loud
and angry. "I say we cannot make a living in this
hard, wild, new country," he was saying. "As soon
as a ship comes, I—for one—am going back."

Even the Allen children knew that if anybody went back to England, that would make it harder and lonelier for the others. They waited to hear what Mr. Bradford would say. His voice was very gentle after the loud, angry one.

"I think," he said, "that we should keep up our hearts and our hopes. We should learn to use the blessings of this new country. This year promises a better harvest than last year."

Before he could say anything more, there rose a dreadful sound from the kitchen. Then Mistress Whiting could be heard weeping and sobbing, "Everything is lost. Everything is spoiled." Mr. Bradford came hurrying out into the kitchen and closed the door behind him.

A month ago Mistress Whiting had covered up her bowl of sugar and set it on a high shelf in the cupboard to keep it safe. But Susan had, just once, peeped in to see how much sugar was there. She had wrapped it up again in its cloth, but she had left the cover only halfway on the bowl. And now when they opened it, they found that mice had slipped in and had been nibbling at it until it was all spoiled. There could be no pudding made of it now. Susan as well as her mother was crying. Not even Mr. Bradford knew what to say or what to do.

Plum Pudding for the Pilgrims

Jane pulled at Robert's sleeve. She was too shy to speak aloud, but the room was quiet for a moment and everyone heard her. "Do you remember what we saw in the woods—the bee tree? Would the bees give us a little honey, do you think, just enough for our pudding? Mother used to make pudding with honey in England."

"Mistress Jane Allen, you are a wise little maid." It was Mr. Bradford's voice that came across the room, and all the women turned round to listen. "If you hurry," he went on, "I think you can get the honey and the pudding can be made ready before the men have stopped talking. They will all feel better when a good supper comes on the table."

Robert and Jane went hurrying out. They ran along the path and into the woods. Three or four of the other boys and girls went with them, Susan Whiting coming last of all. The tears were running down her cheeks, for she knew it was her fault that the sugar had been spoiled. Everybody was anxious to help, but when they came to the bee tree, most of them drew back a little. Everyone is bound to be polite to bees. Only Robert knew what to do.

He had seen woodsmen in England get the honey out of a hive.

He built a fire and put wet leaves on it so that it would smoke. He placed the fire so that the wind would carry the smoke to wrap its cloud all around the tree. There was a loud buzzing at first, then quiet. "Are the bees all dead?" Jane asked anxiously.

"No, the smoke only makes them stupid," Robert said. He had brought his ax, and with one swing of its sharp blade he cut away a big branch. Even the branch was hollow. As it fell, a stream of honey came running out of it. Robert ran a knife into the hole in the trunk and cut out great pieces of new, yellow honeycomb.

The others came forward now to fill the bowls and pails they had brought. Jane had wondered before whether there would be enough honey for a plum pudding. Why, there was enough for the whole village to have pudding every day; enough for sweetening corncakes too—and they had never thought of it before.

The children's voices were loud and gay as they ran back and forth, as busy as the bees had been. Susan Whiting came up to Jane. She was really smiling. "Now I can be happy again," she said.

41

When the pudding was set on the table among the pewter plates and the silver drinking cups, it was the best in the world, so everybody said. Captain Miles Standish ate three plates full, and his face grew redder and redder as he ate. The angry man who had talked so loud leaned back and smiled. "A man always feels better after a good supper," he said, "and a very fine supper this has been."

Governor Bradford had made Robert and Jane sit beside him at the table. Jane was glad that she had put on her best blue homespun skirt and new white kerchief, for everyone was looking at her. Susan Whiting disappeared soon after she had eaten her pudding, but Jane could guess where she had gone. Did not Susan always, every day, go down to the edge of the water to look for a ship from England? In the long summer evening she could still have one more look before darkness came.

When they had all finished eating supper, Governor Bradford got up to speak. But before he had said a word, the door burst open and Susan came running in. "A ship!" she cried. "There's a ship, out by the point. It's sailing into the bay."

It was such great news that, for a minute, no one had a word to say. Governor Bradford spoke at last.

"Before all else, we will give thanks to God," he

said. "We will thank God, not only because the ship has come, but because we have found that we are safe without it. The ship will bring us news from home, it will bring letters, it will bring friends who have followed us to the new country. Perhaps it will bring food, perhaps it will not. Let every person speak the truth—what is the greatest thing that this ship will bring to him?"

All the voices rose at once, the children's too. "Friends, letters, news from England!" If anybody spoke of flour or sugar, his voice was not heard. Perhaps no one did. It had taken them two years to learn it, but these people knew now that they would not go hungry in the new country. They understood that this was a good land, that it held out its blessings more and more to them as they went bravely forward.

CHECKING AIDS FOR TEACHERS

LEVEL: Fifth Reader, early part of book

The Bee Tree

COMPREHENSION CHECKS

Part I Exploring the Woods
Pages 30–33, 740 words

LITERAL COMPREHENSION QUESTIONS

1 Where did Jane Allen live?
   ANSWER: In Plymouth.
2 Who was Jane's best friend?
   ANSWER: Susan Whiting.
3 What did Jane like to do?
   ANSWER: She liked to go to the woods.
4 What did Susan like to do?
   ANSWER: She liked to go to the shore to watch for a ship from England.
5 How did Susan and her family feel about going into the woods?
   ANSWER: They were afraid of the woods.
6 Name four foods the Pilgrims brought to America.

ANSWER: Bacon, flour, salt, and sugar.

7 What were the Pilgrims worried about when they landed
and saw the thick forests?

ANSWER: They were afraid they would not find enough
to eat.

8 Who taught the Pilgrims how to make flour?

ANSWER: The Indians.

9 What did Robert Allen do to help provide food for his
family?

ANSWER: He went hunting and fishing.

10 What was Robert starting out to hunt on the day that
the story took place?

ANSWER: Partridges.

INTERPRETATION QUESTIONS

1 Describe Jane's home as you can picture it from the illus-
tration and details given in the story.

ANSWER: It was a small cabin made of logs and boards;
the bedrooms were upstairs; they were small and directly under the roof.

2 Why do you think Susan was so interested in watching
for the arrival of a ship?

ANSWER: She might have been lonesome and wanted to
get letters from her friends in England; or the family's food supply was low and she might have been
eager to get food and other supplies from England.

3 Which family, the Allens or the Whitings, had a better
chance of taking care of themselves in the new country? Why?

ANSWER: The Allens, because they were willing to go
into the woods to hunt for food.

4 Why did the Pilgrims choose these four foods to bring
to America—bacon, flour, salt, and sugar?

45

ANSWER: None of these were available in America and each filled a definite need. Bacon is a smoked meat and could keep a long time without spoiling; they could make bread from flour; they could use sugar to sweeten berries or wild fruits; they could use salt to flavor their food.

5 Why had Squanto and Robert and Jane learned to make a cry like the call of a wild turkey?

ANSWER: Other wild turkeys, hearing this cry, might come toward it; then they could be killed.

Part II   Jane Finds a Bee Tree
Pages 34–39, 1003 words

LITERAL COMPREHENSION QUESTIONS

1 What strange noise did Jane hear as she picked the flowers in the forest?

ANSWER: She heard a humming and buzzing noise.

2 How did Robert know Jane was under a bee tree?

ANSWER: He saw the holes in the bee tree trunk and the bees going out and in.

3 How did Robert feel about the prosperity of the settlers at that time?

ANSWER: He believed they were having their hardest time.

4 What did Jane do when she tasted the wild plums?

ANSWER: She made a face because they were sour.

5 What were Mistress Allen and Mistress Whiting discussing when Robert and Jane got home?

ANSWER: Supper for the men on Wednesday.

6 What part of the dinner was Mistress Whiting worrying about?

ANSWER: The dessert.

7　What was Jane's idea for a dessert?
　　ANSWER:　To make a plum pudding.
8　Why did Mistress Whiting think it would be a very good
　　　thing to serve the men a sweet pudding just at this
　　　time?
　　ANSWER:　Then nobody could say they were much worse
　　off here than in England.
9　What was the man who was talking to Governor Brad-
　　ford threatening to do?
　　ANSWER:　To return to England on the next ship.
10　What had happened to the bowl of sugar?
　　ANSWER:　The mice had spoiled it.

INTERPRETATION QUESTIONS

1　Why was the buzzing of the bees strange to Jane?
　　ANSWER:　She had never heard any sound like this be-
　　fore; she had never seen or heard bees.
2　Why did Robert pull Jane back?
　　ANSWER:　He didn't want her to get in the way of the bees
　　and get stung.
3　Why was Robert troubled?
　　ANSWER:　He was troubled because he felt some colonists
　　were giving up too easily.
4　For how long would things still be difficult? How do you
　　know?
　　ANSWER:　For at least a year. Mistress Allen had said that
　　it was summer weather at that time. The settlers
　　would have to wait for another crop of corn to be
　　planted and harvested. This would happen a year
　　from September.
5　What do you think the men were going to talk about at
　　their meeting?
　　ANSWER:　How they could meet the problems of living in
　　the new land.

Part III Plum Pudding for the Pilgrims
Pages 40–43, 828 words

LITERAL COMPREHENSION QUESTIONS

1 What idea did Jane have in regard to sweetening the pudding?

ANWER: To get honey from the woods to use in place of sugar for the pudding.

2 What effect did Governor Bradford think a good supper would have on the men?

ANSWER: It would make them feel better.

3 How did Robert plan to get the honey?

ANSWER: He built a fire and put wet leaves on it so that it would smoke; the wind would carry the smoke around the tree and stun the bees.

4 How much honey was there in the tree?

ANSWER: Enough for the whole village to have a pudding every day.

5 How did the children gather the honey?

ANSWER: The children filled bowls and pails with it.

6 What did Captain Miles Standish do that showed how much he enjoyed the pudding?

ANSWER: He ate three plates full.

7 Where did Susan go after she ate the pudding?

ANSWER: To the shore to watch for a ship.

8 What news did Susan have?

ANSWER: A ship from England was arriving in the bay.

9 What would the ship bring?

ANSWER: It would bring letters, news from England, and friends who were following the settlers to the new country.

10 What had taken two years for the settlers to learn?

ANSWER: That they would not go hungry in this new land; that it was a good land.

1 Why did Mr. Bradford think Jane was wise?

   ANSWER: She had used her head and had remembered that honey could be used to sweeten puddings.

2 Why was Mr. Bradford so much concerned about having honey for the pudding?

   ANSWER: Some of the settlers were so dissatisfied that they were threatening to go back to England. He thought that if this country could give them the ingredients for a good dessert, they would feel more like staying.

3 Explain the expression "as busy as bees."

   ANSWER: Bees fly back and forth and work very hard to produce honey.

4 Why was Susan happy again after the honey was gathered?

   ANSWER: She had been responsible for mice getting into the bowl of sugar and spoiling it; now she was glad that she had found a way of replacing the sugar.

5 Why did the settlers use pewter plates and silver drinking cups?

   ANSWER: They had brought these dishes and cups with them from England. There were no earthen or china dishes available in this country.

6 Why did Miles Standish's face get redder and redder?

   ANSWER: He was eating so much that he was getting excited and hot from all the activity.

7 Why did Robert and Jane sit next to Governor Bradford?

   ANSWER: He wanted to honor them for getting the honey which helped make such a good dessert for the colonists?

8 Why did Governor Bradford want all to give thanks to God?

ANSWER: They were a religious people and they wanted to thank God for keeping them safe and showing them that they could get along in this new land.

9 Why wasn't food mentioned when Governor Bradford asked what was the greatest thing the ship could bring?

ANSWER: The settlers realized that this new land was able to supply them with the food they needed.

10 What do you think might be some of the blessings of this land?

ANSWER: The freedom to work and live together and to find ways of improving and building the land.

VOCABULARY CHECKS

Organized for Use in Diagnosing Word Recognition Difficulties

As the child reads the story, check any words in these lists which he doesn't recognize. If you don't wish to place check marks in your book, write the words on a separate piece of paper, then later rearrange them according to the headings given in the "Checking Aids." These groupings will indicate on which of the phonic elements or word structure elements the pupil needs special practice.

PHONICS

INITIAL CONSONANTS

back, bacon, bark, basket, bay, be, beach, beans, beaten, bee, before, behind, berries, best, better, birds, boys, bowl, bound, building, built, burst, bushes, busy, but, buzzing
cabin, call, came, can, captain, carry, caught, colony, coming, cook, corn, could, country, cover, cups, cut

day, dead, deep, deer, dessert, did, dig, disappeared, do, door, down

face, family, far, fast, father, fault, few, fields, find, first, fish, five, followed, food, for, forest, forward, full

garden, gather, gay, get, girls, give, God, going, gone, good

had, hands, happy, hard, harvest, hat, have, heads, hear, hearts, heavy, help, her, him, his, hive, hold, hole, hollow, home, honey, horn, house, how, humming, hundreds, hungry, hunting, hurry, hush

keep, kerchief, kitchen

land, last, later, laughing, leader, leaned, learned, left, legs, letters, lettuce, like, listen, little, lived, lonelier, long, losing, loud, low

make, man, many, meal, meat, meet, men, met, mice, might, miles, minute, mix, moment, more, morning, mother, mouth

new, next, nibbling, night, noise, not, now

pails, parlor, partridges, path, peeped, people, person, pewter, pick, pilgrims, polite, powder, pudding, pulled, purple

ran, raspberries, real, realize, red, remembered, resting, returned, rich, ripe, rivers, roasting, robe, Robert, root, room

safe, said, sailing, salt, same, saved, says, seemed, set, sick, silver, since, so, sobbing, softly, soon, sound, sour, suddenly, summer, sun, supper, Susan

talk, taller, tasted, taught, tears, tell, time, too, together, took, torn, touch, toward, town, turkeys

very, village, voice

waiting, walk, want, was, wasteful, watch, ways, we, weather, Wednesday, week, weeping, well, were, wide, wild, will, William, wind, winter, wish, with, women, wondered, woods, word, worse, would

years, yellow, yet

FINAL CONSONANTS

afraid, ahead, bound, Bradford, bread, cloud, could, dead,
end, England, find, fond, food, forward, found, friend,
grind, God, good, ground, had, head, heard, hold, indeed,
loud, maid, old, red, said, shed, sound, stood, stupid,
toward, would, wild

kerchief, of, off, roof, shelf

bag, dig

bark, cook, look, shook, speak, talk, took, week

all, bowl, feel, full, meal, tell, until, well, will

am, from, him, plum, room, them, William

Allen, cabin, can, corn, down, even, garden, govern, gun,
horn, Indian, kitchen, learn, linen, men, on, open, ran,
seen, soon, sun, Susan, torn, town, when, women

help, keep, sharp, ship, step, up, wrap

brother, cover, deer, farther, father, flour, for, four, gather,
governor, her, mother, other, parlor, powder, queer, remember, shoulder, sour, sugar, summer, together, under,
whether, your

always, as, does, dress, miles, this, unless, us

about, basket, bright, brought, built, but, caught, dessert, eat,
fault, felt, great, hat, hunt, it, left, meet, might, next,
not, out, patient, plant, Robert, salt, set, sight, skirt,
sweet, taught, that, treat, want, wet, what, yet

ax, mix

CONSONANTS WITH TWO OR MORE SOUNDS

Hard c: bacon, because

Soft c: face, lettuce, place, since, voices

Hard g: sugar, bag

Soft g: edge, gentle, partridge, strange, village

s: sight, mistress

s(z): news, use, Susan

s(sh): sugar, sure

blade, blessings, blue
clams, clapped, closed, cloth, cloud
flour, flowers
gladly
place, plans, plant, plates, pleasantly, plenty, plums, Plymouth
slipped
Bradford, branch, brave, bread, bright, bring, brother,
 brought
cry
dreadful, dress, drew, drinking, dry
fresh, friend, from, fruits
great, grew, grind, ground, growing
promises
treat, tree, tried, troubled, true, trunk, truth
skirt
smiled, smoke
speak, spices, spoiled, spoke
starting, steamed, step, still, sting, stood, stopped, stored,
 stupid
sweeten, swing
twelve, twigs, two
strange, strawberries, steam, string, strong
three, throw

MEDIAL BLENDS
troubled, raspberries, wasteful

FINAL BLENDS
best, burst, fast, first, harvest, just, last, must

INITIAL SPEECH SOUNDS
cheeks, children
she, shelf, ship, shook, shore, shoulders, showed, shy

queer, quickly, quiet
than, that, the, them, then, there, these, they
thank, thick, think, thought
what, when, where, whether, which, white, Whiting, why
who, whole

kitchen, farther, father, gather, mother, others, together,
    weather, whether

beach, much, such, touch, watch
enough, laugh
bush, fish, fresh, hush, Standish, wish
back, duck, pick, sick
among, bring, long, string, strong, thing, Whiting
think, trunk
cloth, forth, mouth, path, Plymouth, with

Long a: ate, bacon, brave, came, gave, Jane, late, make,
    patient, place, saved, shade, strange, table, tasted
Short a: am, anxious, as, back, bag, Bradford, can, clapped,
    family, glad, had, happy, has, land, man, planted, ran,
    than, that, wrap
Long e: be, even, evening, these, we
Short e: best, dress, else, empty, end, every, felt, help, left,
    legs, message, next, plenty, rest, set, shed, step, tell, them,
    well, when, yet
Long i: bright, find, grind, kind, like, ripe, sight, smiled,
    spices, time, Whiting, wild
Short i: big, bring, children, dig, finish, fish, give, in, is,
    Indians, little, lived, minute, Pilgrims, rivers, sick, since,
    ship, string, thick, things, this, twigs, village, which,

will, winter, wish, with

Long o: go, holes, knows, low, moment, old, open, spoke, throw, whole

Short o: from, hot, Robert, stop

Long u: used, usually

Short u: buzzing, ducks, hundreds, hunting, just, much, must, plums, such, suddenly, summer, sun, supper, under, until, up, us

Long y: cry, dry, my, why

Short y: angry, carry, colony, every, family, plenty

ai: afraid, pails, sailing, waiting

ay: always, bay, day, gay, saying

ea: beach, beans, each, easily, eat, leaned, leaves, meal, meat, real, speak, steamed, stream, treat

ea: bread, dead, head, heavy, pleasantly, ready

ea: great

ee: bee, deer, feel, keep, meet, peeped, queer, seemed, seen, sweet, three, tree

ie: cried, tried

ie: believe, fields, pieces

oa: roasting

oo: cool, food, room, soon, too

oo: cook, good, look, shook, stood, woods

oi: noise, spoiled

ue: blue, true

ew: few, grew, knew, new

ow: down, flowers, how, now, powder, town

ow: bowl, low, know

ou: about, around, bound, cloud, found, flour, ground, house, loud, out, sour

ou: country, touch, troubled

Vowels followed by r: bark, far, farther, hardest, harvest, parlor, partridges, start, every, her, perhaps, person, pewter, powder, river, Robert, summer, supper, first,

corn, exploring, horn, more, morning, shore, torn, hurried, purple, turkey, turned
Vowels followed by l: all, always, talk, taller

Word Variants

COMPOUND WORDS
afternoon, another, anybody, anything, beside, cannot,
corncake, cupboard, everybody, everywhere, fireplace,
halfway, homespun, honeycomb, housewives, into, Mayflower, nobody, something, sometimes, strawberries,
today, understand, understood, woodsmen

HYPHENATED WORDS
arrow-shaped

INFLECTIONAL ENDINGS
answered, asked, believed, disappeared, finished, harvested,
hurried, landed, learned, liked, lived, looked, loved,
opened, saved, showed, smiled, spoiled, stopped, talked,
tasted, tried, troubled, used, walked, wrapped
greater, harder, lonelier, older, redder
greatest, hardest
berries, comes, clams, ducks, fields, flowers, fruits, hundreds,
months, news, others, Pilgrims, plans, plums, promises,
raspberries, rivers, says, sometimes, squirrels, strawberries, things, trees, turkeys, ways, woods

PREFIXES
across, ago, ahead, along, away, because, before, behind,
disappeared, returned, unless

SUFFIXES
anxiously, bravely, easily, friendly, gladly, lately, pleasantly,

quickly, quietly, really, safely, shyly, softly, suddenly,
   surely
darkness, goodness
dreadful, hopeful, wasteful
beaten, sweeten

POSSESSIVES
Bradford's, brother's, children's, God's, Jane's, King's, Robert's, Susan's

CONTRACTIONS
can't, I'm, there's

NOTE

Reading LUPE'S WISH

In the next story, "Lupe's Wish," there are several words
of Spanish origin. Some of these words are phonetic, however, and easily pronounced and should be counted in the
list of words missed, for example, *Mendoza* (měn dō' sä), *Lupe*
(lo͝o' pā), and *reboso* (rå bō' sō). The following words may be
told to the child and should not be included in his list of
words missed: *Pancho* (pän chō), *Popocatepetl* (pó pō' kä tä'-
pět'l), *tamale* (tạ mä' lē), *tortilla* (tór tē' yä).

LUPE'S WISH

The Mendoza Family

The Mendoza family lived in a little village in a valley near the foot of the volcano Popocatepetl, which in Mexican means "the mountain that smokes."

The father was a charcoal burner and often he was away from home many days at a time watching his fires. Charcoal is made by burning wood which is covered with earth. A charcoal burner knows how much earth to place over the sticks of wood so that they will burn enough to become charcoal but not enough to become ashes.

When he came home, he brought his charcoal and sold it to the people in the village. His son Pancho helped him. If he had any charcoal left over, he saved it for the day when the family would go to the big market. This market was in the city of Puebla.

Early in the morning and late at night the mother was busy making tortillas. First she knelt at her grinding stone and ground corn for tortillas. Then she patted and slapped the moist cornmeal into thin cakes with her hands and baked the cakes on a charcoal stove no bigger than a large pot. Making

tortillas is hard work. It took the mother a long time to make as many tortillas as the family needed for one day.

When the mother was not grinding corn and making tortillas, she sat at her loom weaving beautiful belts. She worked hard to weave many belts so that she, too, would have something to take to market when her husband went with a load of charcoal.

Lupe, the daughter, went to the new school in the village. She liked the school because it had windows that opened to let the fresh air come in. There were no windows in the adobe house in which the Mendoza family lived.

The boys and girls at school planted a vegetable garden, and besides there was a place to play basketball.

Every week a large poster came by mail to the teacher. The teacher put the poster on the wall, and the boys and girls called it their wall newspaper.

The pictures in the wall newspaper told a story. Most of them showed what to do to protect your health. One picture showed that you should sleep at night with your windows open.

It was now vacation time. Lupe was sorry, for she liked to go to school. At home she must now sit every day at a little loom beside her mother and weave belts. While she was weaving, she often thought about the new Health School in Puebla. She had seen a picture of it in the last wall newspaper. If only she could go to the Health School, she could learn to be a real health nurse! If her father had extra charcoal, they might go to the market in Puebla soon. Then she could see the Health School.

Lupe's mother was weaving into her belts the patterns of flowers and leaves which her own mother had taught her, a long time ago. She wove them with red and purple or black and white threads. Lupe was weaving a pattern which she had made up herself. It was a pattern of fruits, vegetables, and flowers, with the figure of a girl.

"That's a funny looking girl," said her mother, looking at the figure Lupe was weaving into a belt.

Lupe did not tell her mother that the girl was a picture of herself as a health nurse.

Lupe's father came home late one afternoon. He had more bags of charcoal than his tired little donkey could carry, so Father carried some of the bags on his back. He thought that it was better for him to get tired than for the donkey to get too tired.

The Mendozas Go to Market

When Lupe saw how much charcoal her father had brought home, she knew that they would be going to market soon. Early the next morning they began to get ready for the great day when they would start for market. Lupe's mother was up long before daylight, making tortillas. Lupe went up the stream to wash the clothes. Pancho and her father went to sell charcoal to the people in the village.

They worked for two days before they were ready for the trip to Puebla. After their clothes were washed and enough tortillas for the journey were baked, Lupe and her mother each had time to weave another belt. The donkey was the only one who did not work. He rested in the pen which Pancho had made for him.

Long before sunrise on the morning of the third day, the father tied a bag of charcoal on each side of the donkey's back. Then the family started on their trip.

The mother carried a basket of tortillas and a bundle of belts. Pancho was dressed just as his father was dressed. He wore loose white trousers and coat, with a big straw sombrero over his dark hair. Lupe, carrying her bundle of belts, looked just as her mother did. She wore a long black skirt almost dragging in the dust and a blue reboso twisted around her head. One end of the reboso hung down over the bundle in her hand.

The early morning air was so cold that it made Lupe's hands and feet ache. But after the Mendozas had walked for two hours, the sun came up, and then the air was warmer.

63

Groups of men and boys carrying bags, and women and girls carrying baskets joined the Mendoza family along the road. Birds in cages, donkeys, pigs, hens, turkeys, and dogs, with their owners, also joined the procession headed for the big market in Puebla. Long before they reached the market building, they heard the voices of people calling to each other. By the time they could see the great square market building, the air was filled with the odor of automobiles, animals, flowers, fish, meat, pineapples, and oranges.

Women were sitting along the edge of the sidewalks cooking tortillas or sweet potatoes over little charcoal stoves. Other women were boiling corn or steaming tamales which rested on a bed of straw above boiling water in the bottom of a kettle.

Soon after the Mendoza family reached the market building, Pancho went with his father to sell charcoal at some of the big houses.

Lupe's New Friend

The market building was crowded with people who had hired the stalls. There was no place inside for Lupe and her mother to sit. So they sat down on the sidewalk and waited for customers. But no one came to buy their belts, and Lupe grew tired of waiting. She left her mother and went inside the market building. As she pushed her way through the crowd, she held out her belts.

She stopped to look at some cheap jewelry, and the merchant noticed her lovely belts. "I'll give you a fine ring for your belts," he said.

The ring which he held up looked like a diamond ring. Lupe wanted it very much, but she knew that the money from her belts was to be used to buy food for the family.

"Come with me," a woman whispered, as she pulled Lupe away. "I will show you where to sell your belts. That man is trying to cheat you."

Lupe followed the woman to a booth where she saw the sign, HEALTH CENTER. "Oh, how I wish that I were a health nurse!" exclaimed Lupe.

"You can be one," said Lupe's new friend. "I am a health nurse. This paper will tell you about the new school. Read it to your father and mother and ask them if you can go to it."

Lupe looked at the nurse's neat blue uniform and also at her brown shoes. She shook her head and said, "I haven't any uniform, or any shoes, or any money to buy them."

"What will you sell your belts for?" asked a woman, coming up to Lupe and taking hold of a belt.

This woman had on a silk dress with flowers printed on it. Lupe thought she was probably a tourist and would pay a good price for the belts.

"I will sell all of them for a pair of brown shoes and a nurse's uniform," she answered.

"Oh, I am afraid I can't give you all that, but I will buy you a pair of shoes for two belts," said the tourist.

"That will be fair," said Lupe's new friend, the health nurse.

The tourist took Lupe to the man who sold shoes. She picked out a pair of brown shoes like the ones the health nurse wore.

Lupe tried on the pair of shoes. It was the first time she had ever worn shoes. They were stiff, and it was hard for her to walk in them. But she was very proud of the shoes, and thanked the tourist. She had two belts left when she went back to her mother.

The Visit to the Health School

Her mother was still sitting on the sidewalk. "Shoes!" she exclaimed as soon as she saw Lupe. "Shoes are no use. You can't eat them. We need food, salt and pepper, and some of the good spices for our chili sauce. I would rather have food than shoes. You should not have given away your belts for the shoes. Think of all the threads you have wasted!"

It was near noon, and the market building was almost empty. Lupe and her mother sat without speaking. Her mother was angry, and Lupe was sorry that she had hurt her mother's feelings. She hid the shoes under her reboso. Soon Pancho and his father came back and sat on the sidewalk beside them. There were no more customers in sight, and the sun was very hot . So they moved across the street and sat in the shade of a doorway.

After what seemed a long time to Lupe, she said, "Can't we go and see the health school? My paper says that the school is behind the Cathedral."

"Yes, we might look at it," said the father.

They walked across the plaza. Soon they passed the black iron fence around the Cathedral. Next they came to a low white building, marked SCHOOL. The nurse who had been at the Health Center in the market that morning was standing in the doorway. She smiled at them and said, "I am glad that you are here. Come with me."

She led them to the end of a long cool hall where a teacher sat at a desk.

"I'd like to come to this school, but I haven't anything except some shoes," said Lupe, holding them up proudly.

"I see you have some belts," said the teacher, looking at the two belts in Lupe's other hand.

"You, too, have some belts," said the teacher to Lupe's mother. "These are very beautiful. I am sure they are worth as much as your daughter's uniforms will cost."

The mother looked at Lupe's eager face. She looked at the kind nurse. And then she said slowly, "Yes, you may have them."

"And when I have charcoal, I will bring you

She led them across the patio to a large room. The walls were covered with brightly-colored pictures of fruits and vegetables. In some of the pictures health nurses were showing people how to take care of foods.

"And I will work in the factory to earn some money for Lupe," said Pancho.

The teacher smiled and said, "Come with me. I will show you the school. When you see it, I think you will be glad to have Lupe stay here."

"The new way seems to be a good way," said the father. "I will be glad to have Lupe stay."

"I think that Lupe will be happy here," said her mother.

"I know I will," Lupe exclaimed joyfully.

Then the teacher wrote "Lupe Mendoza" in a book after the names of the other pupils.

Lupe's wish had come true. She wanted to thank Pancho, and she wanted to tell her mother and father how glad she was that they were going to let her stay. But before she could say any of the things she wanted to say, they had left. All she had time to do was to call after them, "Adios, Adios."

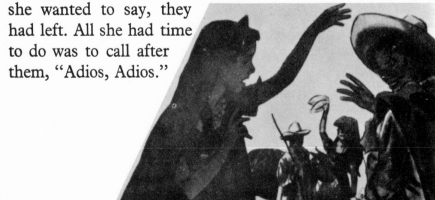

CHECKING AIDS FOR TEACHERS

LEVEL: Fifth Reader, latter part of book

Lupe's Wish

COMPREHENSION CHECKS

Part I   The Mendoza Family
Pages 59–62, 631 words

LITERAL COMPREHENSION QUESTIONS

1 Where did the Mendoza family live?
   ANSWER: In a little village in a valley near the foot of the volcano Popocatepetl; or, in Mexico.

2 What did the father do for a living?
   ANSWER: He was a charcoal burner.

3 How is charcoal made?
   ANSWER: By burning wood covered with earth.

4 What did the mother do?
   ANSWER: She ground corn, made tortillas, and sat at her loom and wove beautiful belts.

5 Name three reasons why Lupe liked school.
   ANSWER: The school had windows to let in fresh air, it had a vegetable garden, and it had a place to play basketball.

6   What was the wall newspaper?

ANSWER: It was a large poster which the teacher put on the wall. The pictures told a story about what to do to protect your health.

7   What did Lupe want to be when she grew up?

ANSWER: She wanted to be a health nurse.

8   Describe the pattern Mrs. Mendoza wove in her belts.

ANSWER: She wove a pattern of fruits, vegetables, and flowers.

9   Whom did the funny-looking figure in Lupe's belt represent?

ANSWER: Lupe as a health nurse.

10   What made Lupe's father so tired?

ANSWER: He had too much charcoal for the donkey to carry, so he had to carry some of it on his back.

INTERPRETATION QUESTIONS

1   Why does a charcoal burner have to be away from home many days at a time?

ANSWER: He has to watch the fire and see that the amount of earth covering the sticks of wood is just right so that the wood will become charcoal and will not burn into ashes.

2   Why did Father save any leftover charcoal for the day the family would go to the city?

ANSWER: He could trade the charcoal for supplies the family might need.

3   Was household work more difficult for Lupe's mother than for your mother? Compare the work of the two women.

ANSWER: Lupe's mother had to grind her own corn with a grinding stone, cook food for the family on a small charcoal stove, and weave belts to sell at market. My mother buys corn in cans or frozen packages; she cooks on a gas or electric stove; she does no weaving; she buys belts and other clothing ready-made.

4 Why do you think Lupe wanted to be a nurse?

ANSWER: She probably wanted to be a nurse so that she could teach the people in her village better ways of taking care of themselves; or, she wanted to live a better life than her mother was living.

5 What determined how often the Mendoza family went to market?

ANSWER: It depended on how much charcoal the father sold to the people in the village and how much he had left over to sell in the big market.

6 Which pattern do you think the more original, the mother's or Lupe's? Why?

ANSWER: Lupe's. The mother just wove designs she had been taught, but Lupe used her imagination and made up designs.

7 Why was Lupe weaving belts?

ANSWER: She was weaving belts to help the family make a living; her belts could be traded for supplies the family might need.

8 Why did Lupe's mother think the girl in Lupe's belt funny?

ANSWER: She had never seen such a girl woven in a belt; she didn't know it was a picture of Lupe as a health nurse.

9 How did Father show that he was considerate of the donkey?

ANSWER: He didn't overload the donkey with charcoal; he carried some of the bags of charcoal on his own back.

10 Why did Father think it better for him to get tired than for the donkey to get tired?

ANSWER: If the donkey got too tired he wouldn't move and Father would not be able to get his charcoal to market.

Part II   The Mendozas Go to Market
Pages 62–65, 429 words

1 How did Lupe know that the family would soon go to market?

ANSWER: She saw that her father had brought home a great deal of charcoal.

2 What three things did the Mendozas do to get ready for the trip?

ANSWER: They made tortillas, washed their clothes, and wove belts.

3 How long did it take the Mendozas to get ready for the trip?

ANSWER: They worked for two days to get ready.

4 What made Lupe uncomfortable during the early part of the trip?

ANSWER: The cold made her hands and feet ache.

5 How did the family get to the city?

ANSWER: They walked.

6 Tell how Pancho was dressed and how Lupe was dressed.

ANSWER: Pancho wore loose white trousers, a coat, and a big straw sombrero. Lupe wore a long black skirt and a blue reboso twisted around her head.

7 What were some of the other people bringing to market?

ANSWER: Birds in cages, donkeys, pigs, hens, and turkeys.

8 Name some of the odors that filled the air.

ANSWER: Odors of automobiles, animals, flowers, fish, meat, pineapples, and oranges.

9 What were women on the sidewalks cooking?

ANSWER: They were cooking tortillas, sweet potatoes, corn, and tamales.

10 How were the corn and the tamales cooked?

ANSWER: The corn was boiled; the tamales were steamed by resting them on a bed of straw above boiling water.

INTERPRETATION QUESTIONS

1 Why did the Mendoza family wash their clothes in the stream?

ANSWER: They didn't have a washing machine and probably they did not have running water in their home.

2 Why did Lupe and her mother do all the things they did before they were ready for the trip?

ANSWER: They wanted the family to have clean clothes to wear; they had to have tortillas for food during the trip; they wanted to have as many belts as possible to sell.

3 Why did Pancho and his father sell charcoal in the village when they were about to go to the city to sell charcoal?

ANSWER: They had more charcoal than the donkey could carry to the city; or, perhaps the father wanted some money to take along in case of an emergency.

4 Why did the family have to start on their trip before sunrise?

ANSWER: They wanted to spend as much of the day as possible at the market.

5 Why was the morning air so cold?

ANSWER: They lived in a mountainous region.

6   What do you think going to market meant to the Mendoza family?

ANSWER: It meant a chance to sell the things they had and to buy supplies they needed.

7   What do you think the men and boys had in the bags they were carrying and what do you think the women and girls had in their baskets?

ANSWER: The men and boys probably had charcoal; the women and girls probably had belts in their baskets, or perhaps tortillas for food.

8   For what purpose were the women cooking at the edge of the sidewalks?

ANSWER: They wanted to sell food to the people who came to the market and make a little money.

9   Why was charcoal so important a product?

ANSWER: It was the chief fuel for cooking in Mexican homes at that time.

10   Why did Father and Pancho go to the big houses to sell charcoal instead of staying in the market place?

ANSWER: Probably they thought they would be able to sell more charcoal to the people in the big houses.

Part III   Lupe's New Friend
Pages 65–67, 441 words

LITERAL COMPREHENSION QUESTIONS

1   What did Lupe and her mother do in an attempt to sell their belts?

ANSWER: They sat on the sidewalk and waited for customers.

2   What did Lupe do when she became tired of waiting for someone to buy their belts?

ANSWER: She left her mother and went inside the market building and tried to sell her belts there.

3   What happened at the jewelry stall?

ANSWER: A man tried to give her a fake diamond ring for her belts.

4   Why didn't Lupe trade her belts for the ring?

ANSWER: She knew that money for her belts was needed to buy food for the family.

5   Who was the woman who said she would show Lupe where to sell her belts?

ANSWER: A health nurse.

6   How was she dressed?

ANSWER: She wore a neat blue uniform and brown shoes.

7   What did she tell Lupe to do?

ANSWER: To read a paper about the new school to her father and mother.

8   What made Lupe think the woman who came up to her was a tourist?

ANSWER: She wore a silk dress with flowers printed on it.

9   How was Lupe able to get the shoes?

ANSWER: She traded two belts for a pair of shoes.

10 How did Lupe feel about her new shoes?

ANSWER: She was proud of them, even though it was hard for her to walk in them.

INTERPRETATION QUESTIONS

1   Who do you think the people were that had hired the stalls in the market building?

ANSWER: People who had all kinds of things to sell.

2   Why was the jewelry merchant so quick to offer Lupe a cheap ring for her belts?

ANSWER: He had noticed that they were unusually lovely and he thought he could sell them for a good price.

77

3 Why did the nurse tell Lupe to read the paper to her parents?

ANSWER: Probably because her parents had not attended school and did not know how to read.

4 Why did the nurse pick out Lupe from the crowd and take her to the Health Center?

ANSWER: Because she thought Lupe would be a good prospect for the new school.

5 What do you think the purpose of the new school was?

ANSWER: The purpose probably was to train nurses and to prepare and send out materials to help improve the health of the Mexican people.

6 Why was Lupe discouraged when she looked at the nurse?

ANSWER: Lupe needed a uniform to be a nurse, and she had no money to buy one.

7 Why was it better to sell things to a tourist than to a native?

ANSWER: Tourists had more money to spend than the natives, and so they paid more for the things the natives had to sell.

8 Do you think Lupe's offer to sell all four of her belts for a pair of shoes and a nurse's uniform was a fair offer? Why or why not?

ANSWER: No. Her belts weren't worth as much as both of these things would cost.

9 Why hadn't Lupe ever worn shoes before?

ANSWER: It was not the custom to wear shoes in her village; also shoes cost money and Lupe's family could not afford to buy them.

10 Why was Lupe proud of the shoes?

ANSWER: It was the first pair she had ever owned; or, it might have made her feel important to have them since probably few people in her village wore them.

Literal Comprehension Questions

1   What seasonings did the mother say that the family needed?
    ANSWER: Salt, pepper, and spices.

2   When there were no customers and the sun became hot, what did the family do?
    ANSWER: They moved across the street and sat in the shade of a doorway.

3   Where was the Health School located?
    ANSWER: It was located behind the cathedral.

4   Who welcomed them to the school?
    ANSWER: The nurse who had been at the Health Center in the market that morning.

5   Where did she take the family when they first came in?
    ANSWER: She led them to the end of a long, cool hall.

6   How did Lupe's mother help to get Lupe's uniform?
    ANSWER: She gave the nurse the belts that she had left.

7   How was the father going to help Lupe?
    ANSWER: He would bring charcoal to her.

8   How would Pancho help Lupe?
    ANSWER: He would work in the factory and earn money for Lupe.

9   What did the teacher do to show that Lupe was accepted at school?
    ANSWER: She wrote "Lupe Mendoza" in a book after the names of the other pupils.

10 Did Lupe thank her family? Why or why not?
    ANSWER: No, because before she could say any of the things she wanted to say to her family, they had left.

INTERPRETATION QUESTIONS

1 What did Lupe's mother mean when she said, "Think of all the threads you have wasted"?

   ANSWER: It had taken many threads to make the belts. Now she had traded the belts for shoes which the mother considered to be useless.

2 Why was the market building almost empty near noon?

   ANSWER: It was very warm at noon so the people were keeping quiet, or the people were eating lunch.

3 Why did the mother say "slowly" that the nurse could have the belts?

   ANSWER: The belts were needed to buy food, so she was reluctant to give them away.

4 Why were pictures especially necessary in giving health information in this situation?

   ANSWER: Many people were not able to read, so the health nurses used pictures to show them ways of keeping themselves and their children healthy.

5 What was the significance of the father's decision when he said, "The new way seems to be a good way. I will be glad to have Lupe stay"?

   ANSWER: He realized that progress was taking place and that better ways of living were being developed. He wanted his daughter to have an education and to learn these ways.

VOCABULARY CHECKS

Organized for Use in Diagnosing Word Recognition Difficulties

As the child reads the story, check any words in these lists which he doesn't recognize. If you don't wish to place check marks in your book, write the words on a separate piece of paper, then later rearrange them according to the headings given in the "Checking Aids." These groupings will indicate the phonic elements and the word structure elements on which the pupil needs special practice.

PHONICS

INITIAL CONSONANTS

baby, back, bag, baked, bamboos, banana, basket, beautiful, because, before, began, belt, bench, beside, better, big, birds, boiling, book, booth, bottom, boy, building, bundle, burn, busy, but, buy

cages, cakes, calling, came, care, carry, cathedral, coat, cold, cool, come, corn, could, covered, customers

dark, daughter, day, desk, diamond, did, donkey, doors, down, dust

factory, fair, family, father, feather, feelings, feet, fence, figure, fine, fires, first, fish, followed, food, foot, found

garden, gazed, get, girl, give, go, good, got

hair, hall, hands, hard, hat, headed, health, helped, hen, hid, him, hired, home, hour, house, how, hung, hurt, husband

jewelry, joined, journey, just

kettle, kind

large, last, late, learn, leaves, led, left, let, little, lived, load, looking, loom, loose, long, lovely, low, Lupe

made, mail, make, many, market, means, meat, men, Mendoza, merchant, Mexican, moist, money, more, morning, most, mother, mountain, mouth, much

near, neat, need, new, next, night, noticed, nurse

pair, palms, paper, patio, patterns, pen, people, pepper, picture, piece, pig, poster, pot, potatoes, Puebla, purple, put

rather, reached, read, ready, real, reboso, red, rested, ring, road, room salt, sat, sauce, save, seems, seen, sell, side, silk, silver, sight, sit, sold, sombrero, some, soon, son, sorry, sun

take, talk, taught, teacher, tell, tied, time, tired, told, took, tourist, turkeys

vacations, valley, vegetable, village, visit, volcano

walk, wall, warmer, was, wash, wasted, watch, water, way, wear, weave, week, went, were, will, windows, with, wood, women, wore, work, world, worn, worth, would, wove

yes

FINAL CONSONANTS

clinic

bed, cold, could, diamond, did, food, glad, had, hand, hard, heard, held, hid, husband, load, need, old, proud, read, red, road, should, sold, third, thousand, tired, told, wood, world, would

bag, big

cathedral, charcoal, cool, girl, mail, oil, real, sell, tell, wall, will

bottom, from, him, loom, room, them, uniform

brown, burn, clean, corn, down, earn, garden, iron, learn, men, Mexican, mountain, noon, often, open, own, pattern, pen, procession, seen, soon, son, then, thin, vacation, when, women

sleep, trip, up

after, air, better, daughter, eager, father, hair, mother, near, odor, over, paper, pepper, poster, rather, silver, teacher, their, your

adios, is, overalls, precious, this, was

about, but, cheat, coat, eat, eight, except, foot, get, great, heat, knelt, left, let, market, meat, might, neat, night, not, pot, protect, salt, sat, skirt, street, sweet, taught, that, thought, went, what

Hard c: factory, picture, vacation

Soft c: center, city, fence, noticed, peace, place, procession, sauces, spices, voices

Hard g: began, eager, figure, bigger

Soft g: edges, large, oranges, strange, vegetables, village

INITIAL BLENDS

black, blue

clean, clinic, clothes

flowers

glad

place, planted, plaza

slapped, sleep, slowly

brightly, brought, brown

crowd

dragging, dress

fresh, friend, from, fruits

great, grew, grind, ground, groups

precious, printed, procession, protect, proud

tried, trip, trousers, true

skirt

smiled, smokes

speaking, spices

stand, stay, steaming, stepped, sticks, stiff, still, stopped, stove

twisted

screens

spread

strange, straw, stream, street

school

threads, through

FINAL BLENDS

ask, desk   cost, first, last, moist, tourist

charcoal, cheap, cheat, chili
shade, she, shoes, shook, should, show
than, that, them, then, there, they
thanked, thin, think, third, thought
what, when, where, which, while, whispered, white

MEDIAL SPEECH SOUNDS
merchant, Pancho, watching
ashes
clothes, father, mother, other
cathedral, something

FINAL SPEECH SOUNDS
bench, each, much, reach, watch, which
fish, fresh, push, wash, wish
back, stick
among, hung, long, ring
booth, earth, health, mouth, worth

VOWEL SOUNDS
Long a: ache, baked, cages, cake, came, late, made, make, paper, place, save, shade, take, wasted
Short a: am, animals, ashes, back, bag, black, can, dragging, factory, family, glad, had, hands, have, patted, pattern, planted, sat, slapped, stand, thanked, that, valley
Long e: he, she
Short e: belt, bench, better, center, dressed, empty, end, held, help, hens, kettle, knelt, led, left, Mendoza, Mexican, next, pen, pepper, precious, red, rested, sell, tell, them, then, went, when
Long i: diamond, fine, fire, grind, hired, iron, liked, price, sight, smiled, spices, time, while, white, wire
Short i: big, city, clinic, did, figures, fish, hid, his, in, little,

live, picked, picture, pigs, ring, silver, sit, sticks, stiff, thin, think, this, trip, twisted, village, whispered, will, windows, wish, with

Long o: clothes, cold, go, hold, home, odor, only, open, over, poster, reboso, smokes, sold, stone, stove, wove

Short o: bottom, donkey, from, not, pocketful, pot, probably, sombrero, stopped, volcano

Long u: uniform, use

Short u: bundle, but, customers, dust, funny, hung, husband, just, must, sun

Long y: buy

Short y: angry, baby, carry, city, early, electricity, factory, family, funny, jewelry, money, ready, sorry, story

ai: afraid, exclaimed, mail, waited

ay: day, may, play

au: because, daughter, sauce, taught

aw: straw

ea: clean, cheap, cheat, each, eager, ears, eat, leaves, means, nearer, reached, real, speaking, steaming, weave

ea: headed, health, ready, spread, threads, wear

ea: great

ee: feelings, needs, screens, seemed, sweet, week

ew: knew, new

ey: donkey, turkey

ie: tied

ie: piece

oa: charcoal, coat, load, road

oo: bamboos, booth, cool, loom, loose, noon, room, school, soon, too

oo: book, cooking, foot, good, look, shook, took, wood

oi: boiling, joined, moist, oil, voices

oy: boys

ou: about, aloud, around, found, ground, house, mountains, proud, thousand, trousers *ou:* brought, thought

ou: groups, through, tourist

ow: low, owners, show, windows

ow: brown, crowd, down, how, flowers

Vowels followed by r: charcoal, farther, garden, hard, large, market, herself, merchant, paper, patterns, birds, first, girl, skirt, third, betorn, corn, more, morning, tortillas, uniform, wore, work, world, worth, burn, hurt, journey, nurse, purple, turned

Vowels followed by l or w: salt, stalk, walked, wall, straw

WORD VARIANTS

COMPOUND WORDS

afternoon, another, anything, basketball, because, become, before, beside, cornmeal, daylight, doorway, herself, inside, into, newspaper, pineapples, sidewalk, something, sunrise, without

HYPHENATED WORDS

black-eyed, brightly-colored

INFLECTIONAL ENDINGS

baked, called, carried, covered, crowded, dressed, filled, followed, headed, helped, joined, looked, marked, needed, opened, patted, planted, printed, pushed, reached, rested, showed, stopped, slapped, started, thanked, twisted, waited, walked, wanted, wasted, whispered

bigger, burner, teacher, warmer

baking, boiling, burning, calling, carrying, cooking, dragging, grinding, hiding, making, morning, sitting, speaking, steaming, taking, trying, watching, weaving

animals, ashes, automobiles, bags, belts, baskets, bamboos, boys, cakes, cages, customers, dogs, fires, flowers, fruits, girls, groups, hands, hens, houses, leaves, Mendozas, machines, nurses, oranges, owners, palms, patterns, pesos, pictures, pigs, plants, screens, sidewalks, smokes, spices, sticks, threads, tortillas, turkeys, voices, windows

PREFIXES
across, ago, along, around, away
become, behind
exclaim, except
procession, protect

SUFFIXES
brightly, joyfully, proudly, slowly
feathery
funny
shady
beautiful, pocketful
tourist

CONTRACTIONS
can't, haven't, I'd, that's

POSSESSIVES
donkey's, Lupe's, mother's, nurse's

STAR'S DREAM

Star and the Great Hunter

"I wish Father and Star would come," said White Cloud. "We've had nothing but fish to eat for two days. Perhaps they will bring a wild pig."

"Or an antelope," her mother added. "I like antelope better than pig. But both taste good when they are roasted over an oak-wood fire."

White Cloud cut a thread from a sinew and threaded her needle. She cut the thread with a flint knife which had two sawtooth edges. The needle was a smooth piece of bone with an eye at one end and a sharp point at the other.

"Star is clever," said White Cloud as she sewed skins together to make a shirt. "He may get a young pig, while Father may kill an antelope. Then we shall have enough meat for a feast. We can ask our friends to eat with us."

White Cloud was much too hopeful, however. When her father and brother came up the slope, they carried only some chunks of horse meat in their skin bags.

"We should not have had even this," said Standing Bull, "if Great Hunter, the lion, had not killed meat. We waited till the lion ate all it wanted and went away. Then we cut some pieces off what was left."

"But will the lion be angry?" asked White Cloud's mother. "If it is, it will drive all the game away."

"Don't worry about that," Standing Bull answered. "Star spoke to Great Hunter when we went for the meat, but the lion only looked at us. Then, while Star wrapped his pieces in skin, I sang a song of thanks:

> Great Hunter, we thank you;
> We thank you for this meat.
> We are glad we came, Great Hunter,
> When you left meat for us.

"I think the lion liked my song. Perhaps it will kill another horse when we become hungry tomorrow."

White Cloud brought sticks for a fire while her mother cut the meat into strips. Star scraped new, sharp points on the sticks that were used to hold the strips in the fire while they were roasting. This really was girl's work, but Star was too hungry to wait for White Cloud to do it. Since no one was watching, she did not care. But if her friends had been near, she would have told him to stop. She would not have wanted her friends to laugh and tease her, saying, "White Cloud is so slow that her brother has to sharpen the roasting sticks!"

Star, his sister, and their parents lived about 15,000 years ago in what is now southern France. Their home was a sheltered place under an overhanging cliff. This made all the shelter they needed on sunny summer days. When cold or rain came, the women spread skin blankets over a framework made of poles. When the blankets were tied to the poles, they made warm shelters which were protected by the cliff. Almost a hundred people lived in blanket houses under that one rock shelter.

The chief of the tribe came to Star's father after supper was eaten. "Standing Bull," said the chief, "meat is scarce; some people do not even have fish. It is said that the lion gave you a horse. This means that Great Hunter likes you. Therefore I come to you for counsel. How may our people find food?"

Standing Bull spread a wolf robe for the chief, and the two men sat down. Each knew just what he should do and say, for the cave people had old, old customs for just such times as this. The chief must sit and look at the fire, while Standing Bull pretended to think deeply.

At last Standing Bull cleared his throat and spoke. "It is true that food is scarce," he said. "It is true, also, that we have had meat given us by Great Hunter, the lion. In the fir thicket, he made magic which helped him kill a horse.

"Let us make magic, too. Let us go to the Cave of Paintings. There we may make new pictures and sing songs which Great Hunter will hear."

"Your counsel is good," answered the chief. "I shall tell the other singers and painters. We shall go at daybreak tomorrow!"

"One more thing," said Standing Bull, and this time he really thought hard. "The lion did not give the meat to me, but to my son, Star. My son heard Great Hunter eating; he said soft words so that the lion did not attack us when we went to get the meat. The boy is learning to draw, also. Let him go with us to the cave."

"No boy has ever gone there," the chief objected.

"But what other boy has talked to the Great Hunter? What other boy has found meat when grown men could not catch fish? What other boy can draw a bison like this with a sharp flint tool?"

"None," the chief admitted. "Let your son come with you to the cave. He may wait in the first room while we go into the next room to paint and sing. Tell him to be ready early!"

In the Cave of Paintings

Star did not need to be told. He was up long before his father, putting his flint and his stone lamp into a leather pouch. As he started out for the cave, White Cloud whispered, "Find out where Father can kill a bison. Then I can tan its robe for you, to make a good, warm bed."

On the long walk to the cave Star thought about a bison. He thought about it still more when he got there, for the limestone walls were covered with pictures of these big animals. The pictures were dark red and brownish, shaded with black. Other paintings showed mammoths, wild pigs, and wolves. A black one pictured a shaggy horse galloping away from an animal that was chasing it.

When the men went into the next room in the cave, Star lighted his stone lamp. It was filled with bear grease that burned on a moss wick. Star could now see the paintings plainly, and he kept on looking at them even when the men began to sing.

The song was a low short chant, only a few words, repeated over and over. The words were very, very old—so old that even the chief had forgotten what they meant. But they sounded like hunting and eating. Star felt sure that these words and the new pictures would bring plenty of game. Perhaps they would bring the big bison that White Cloud had told him to find.

Star did not intend to fall asleep but in a short time he was asleep and dreaming. The painted mammoths and bison on the walls started to move. They were walking across open plains or stopping to eat grass and herbs. The mammoths pulled up bushes, scattering little balls of dirt on their heads. The bison sometimes rested, chewing their cuds. One of them, however, wandered to one side and was frightened by a lion. Away went the bison at a gallop, leaving Great Hunter far behind. The bison went on and on, until it came to the edge of a cliff.

Star gasped and awoke. That cliff looked like the one above the Cave of Paintings! No doubt about it—that big bison was eating grass in the meadow almost above Star's head!

The boy did not call his father, for it was bad luck to interrupt hunting songs. Star hardly knew

what to do, until he saw the painted robe which his father had left on the floor. It had broad red, white, and black stripes. Star tucked it under his arm and ran to the mouth of the cave.

Star Finds a Bison

Coming out, he moved carefully. He walked along the ledge to a place that was uneven enough for climbing. He scrambled upward from one rock to the next, taking care not to make a loud noise.

If a stone slipped, the noise might alarm the bison. Star knew that the beast would get away unless he took it by surprise.

At last Star got his head above the top of the cliff. As he did so, his heart gave a jump. Suppose there was no bison, after all! Suppose he had not had a vision, but just an everyday dream!

But the bison was there—the biggest bison Star had ever seen. It stood near the edge of the cliff, looking sleepy. In a moment it lay down, grunted, and began to chew its cud. Star could see its smooth sides go in and out as it took deep, slow breaths.

Carefully Star crept forward, wriggling along on his stomach from one shrub to the next. When he reached the last bush, he stopped and took a tight hold on two corners of the striped robe. Then he leaped up and ran toward the bison, shouting and waving the robe.

When the animal heard Star, it got up and started to run away. It must have forgotten about the cliff, for it jumped sidewise twice before it turned. That was one jump too many; as it whirled, its hind legs slipped and went over the edge. It tried to catch itself but could not; its front feet slipped, too. In a moment the animal plunged down to the ledge that led to the mouth of the cave.

The chief, far back in the cave, heard the noise. He did not stop the singing, but he did whisper to Star's father:

"I heard a noise like something falling. Go out and see what is wrong. If enemies have come, bring Star. No one can harm us in here, for we can keep people from coming through the narrow passageway."

Standing Bull wriggled out through the passageway and looked about the main cavern. He found Star's lamp on the floor, with its wick almost burned away. But Star was gone. Why had he wandered away while the men were painting and chanting?

Standing Bull went to the mouth of the cave and looked out. Star was running along the ledge toward a huge dead bison. "I killed it, Father! I killed it! While I was sleeping, the Great Hunter showed me this bison in a vision. I awoke, ran to the top of the hill, and frightened it so that it fell over the cliff."

Standing Bull was amazed; magic seldom worked so quickly. Still, he knew the spirits did strange things.

Just then the men stopped painting and chanting and began to come out of the cave. They looked at the bison and at Star and his father. Then Star's father told them to stand in a ring. He pulled out

his best knife, broke it, and laid it on the bison's
head while he chanted:

"Great Hunter, I thank you;
  I thank you for the tribe and my son.

  This flint knife is sharp; I break it.
  Your help is more than a knife;
  Your help brings more food than it can cut.

  Great Hunter, I thank you;
  I thank you for the tribe and my son."

Star and the men did not say a word, but their
faces showed that they, too, thanked the Great
Hunter.

CHECKING AIDS FOR TEACHERS

LEVEL: Sixth Reader, early part of book

Star's Dream

COMPREHENSION CHECKS

Part I Star and the Great Hunter
Pages 88–92, 858 words

LITERAL COMPREHENSION QUESTIONS

1 What were White Cloud and her mother hoping that Father and Star would bring them?

ANSWER: They wished that Father and Star would bring them a wild pig or an antelope.

2 Describe the needle and thread that White Cloud used for sewing.

ANSWER: The thread was cut from a sinew with a flint knife; the needle was a smooth piece of bone with an eye at one end and a sharp point at the other.

3 What was White Cloud sewing?

ANSWER: She was making a shirt for Star by sewing animal skins together.

4 What kind of meat did Father and Star bring home?

ANSWER: They brought home some chunks of horse meat.

5 How did Star and Standing Bull manage to get this horse meat?

ANSWER: They waited until a lion killed the animal and ate all it wanted; they then cut some pieces off what was left.

6 When and where did Star's family live?

ANSWER: They lived about 15,000 years ago in what is now southern France.

7 Describe Star's home.

ANSWER: It was a sheltered place under an overhanging cliff. The women spread skin blankets over a framework of poles to protect their families from cold or rain.

8 What was troubling the chief of the tribe?

ANSWER: The problem of how his people might find more food.

9 What was Standing Bull's advice?

ANSWER: To make magic, by going to the Cave of Paintings and painting new pictures, and by singing songs to the Great Hunter.

10 What reasons did Standing Bull give for requesting that Star be permitted to go to the Cave of Paintings?

ANSWER: Star had talked to the Great Hunter; he had found meat when grown men could not catch fish; he could draw with a sharp flint tool.

INTERPRETATION QUESTIONS

1 Why was White Cloud's knife made from flint?

ANSWER: People didn't know how to make steel in those days, so they took a hard piece of rock called flint and rubbed it down and made it sharp.

2   Why was White Cloud hopeful?

    ANSWER: She knew that her father and Star were good hunters and she was confident that they would kill an animal and bring it back home.

3   What does Standing Bull's explanation of why the lion wouldn't be angry tell you about the religion of these people?

    ANSWER: They worshiped the lion as if it were a god.

4   Why were the houses called blanket houses?

    ANSWER: They were called blanket houses because they were made of skin blankets spread over poles.

5   Why did the chief come to Standing Bull for counsel?

    ANSWER: Standing Bull's family was the only family that had enough meat, so he thought Great Hunter favored Standing Bull and he wanted Standing Bull's advice in order to help the other people.

6   Judging from this story, what kind of a government did these people have?

    ANSWER: It was a one-man government ruled by a chief, but this chief didn't make all decisions unaided; he sought advice from members of the tribe.

7   Why did Standing Bull pretend to think deeply?

    ANSWER: This was the way he was expected to act when the chief asked his advice.

8   Why did Standing Bull think magic would help them?

    ANSWER: He believed that it was through magic that the lion had been able to kill the horse.

9   How do you visualize the inside of the Cave of Paintings?

    ANSWER: A large, dark cavern with walls of rock on which men had carved and colored in outlines of animals.

10   Why had no boy ever gone to the cave before?

ANSWER: It was one of the old customs of the tribe that only grown men were permitted to enter the cave to paint, sing, and ask favors of the Great Hunter.

Part II In the Cave of Paintings
Pages 92–94, 435 words

LITERAL COMPREHENSION QUESTIONS

1 What did Star do to get ready to go to the cave?
ANSWER: He got up early and put his flint and his stone lamp into a leather pouch.

2 What did White Cloud want Star to find out? Why?
ANSWER: She wanted him to find out where Father could kill a bison so she could tan its robe for Star, to make a good, warm bed.

3 What animal was Star thinking about on his long walk to the cave?
ANSWER: He was thinking about a bison.

4 What were the colors of the pictures in the cave?
ANSWER: They were dark red and brownish, shaded with black.

5 Name some of the animals painted on the wall.
ANSWER: Mammoths, bison, wild pigs, wolves, a shaggy horse.

6 What did Star do to enable him to see the pictures on the wall?
ANSWER: He lighted his stone lamp.

7 What was Star's dream?
ANSWER: He dreamed that the painted bison and mammoths were moving about; that they were walking across the plains or eating grass and herbs; that the bison was at the edge of a cliff.

8 Star gasped when he awoke. Why?

ANSWER: The cliff that the bison was standing on looked like the one above the Cave of Paintings.

9 What was the bison doing?

ANSWER: He was eating grass in the meadow almost above Star's head.

10 What did Star do?

ANSWER: He took his father's robe and ran to the mouth of the cave.

INTERPRETATION QUESTIONS

1 Why didn't Star have to be told to get up early on the morning of the trip to the cave?

ANSWER: He was anxious to go into the cave.

2 Is there anything in this story that would cause you to believe that these people belonged to the Stone Age? If so, what?

ANSWER: White Cloud cut the thread with a flint knife and Star drew the bison with a flint tool; or they used flint tools.

3 How do you think the cavemen got the colors to use in painting?

ANSWER: Since the colors were brown and red and black, they probably used soils of various colors mixed with something else, perhaps grease.

4 Is there anything in this story which would indicate that some of the people were talented and others weren't? If so, what?

ANSWER: Yes. The chief said that he would tell the other singers and painters. He didn't say he would tell everyone.

5 Would you say that these people were clever? Give proof of your answer.

ANSWER: Yes. They could make thread from sinews, needles from flint, other tools from stone, paint colored pictures, construct shelters with skin blankets.

6 Why do you think Star dreamed about the bison?
ANSWER: His sister had talked to him about a bison before he left for the cave and he had been thinking about the bison before he fell asleep.

7 Do you think Star's dream was important? Why?
ANSWER: Yes. His dream seemed to predict where he would find a bison.

8 If Star's dream were prophetic of what might happen, what is the significance of the explanation concerning the bison's separation from its herd?
ANSWER: It would be easier to kill a bison if he were alone rather than in a herd.

9 Why might it bring bad luck to interrupt hunting songs?
ANSWER: The people thought that the Great Hunter might get angry and not help the men find food; then the tribe would have to go hungry.

10 Why did Star take the painted robe that his father had left?
ANSWER: He thought he might use it to frighten the bison.

Part III Star Finds a Bison
Pages 94–97, 587 words

LITERAL COMPREHENSION QUESTIONS

1 Star moved carefully on the ledge. Why?
ANSWER: He did not want to make any noise that might frighten the bison away.

2 What was the bison doing when Star saw it?
ANSWER: It was lying down chewing its cud.

3 How did Star move forward?

   ANSWER: He carefully crept forward, wriggling along on his stomach from one shrub to the next.

4 How did the bison try to escape?

   ANSWER: It started to run away and tried to jump sideways.

5 How did Star kill the bison?

   ANSWER: He ran toward it, shouting and waving the robe; the bison became frightened and fell over the cliff.

6 When the chief heard the noise, who did he think might have come?

   ANSWER: Enemies.

7 What made the chief feel the men in the cave were safe?

   ANSWER: He thought the men were safe because they could keep people from coming in through the narrow passageway.

8 What did Standing Bull wonder about when he found that Star was gone?

   ANSWER: He wondered why Star had wandered away while the men were painting and chanting.

9 What did Star's father do when the men came out of the cave?

   ANSWER: He asked them to stand in a ring. Then he sang a song of thanks to the Great Hunter.

10 In what way was it evident that the men, too, were thankful to the Great Hunter?

   ANSWER: Their faces showed that they were thankful.

Interpretation Questions

1 What distinction do you think Star made between a vision and a dream?

ANSWER: A dream to him was just a series of thoughts which one might have while sleeping; a vision was a distinct scene revealed to him by supernatural power, in this case by the Great Hunter to whom the men were singing and chanting.

2 The story says the bison "began to chew its cud." What does this mean?

ANSWER: It means that the bison was beginning to bring the grass that he had eaten back from his stomach to his mouth for rechewing. The portion that comes up for rechewing is called a "cud."

3 What plan did Star have in mind when he waved the robe?

ANSWER: He wanted to confuse the bison so that it would fall over the cliff.

4 What might have happened if the bison had decided not to run away?

ANSWER: He might have killed Star.

5 Why didn't the chief stop the singing?

ANSWER: He was afraid that if he stopped the singing, this would displease the Great Hunter.

6 Who might have been the enemies of this tribe?

ANSWER: Men in other tribes who envied these men their hunting ground, or who envied them their singing and painting cave.

7 Do you think the chief might have been too optimistic in thinking the enemies could not harm the men because they could be prevented from coming through the narrow passageway? Is there anything else that the enemy might have done to harm the men? If so, what?

ANSWER: Yes. They might have blocked the passageway and shut the men in the cave.

8   How did Standing Bull account for the bison coming to them so soon?

    ANSWER: He thought it was because of the magic they had worked through their singing and painting.

9   Why was Star's father the one to sing the song of thanks?

    ANSWER: He sang the song because his son was a hero, or because he was the one who had suggested going to the cave to make magic.

10 Why did Standing Bull break his knife?

    ANSWER: He thought that the Great Hunter's magic was more powerful than his knife in getting food for the tribe.

VOCABULARY CHECKS

Organized for Use in Diagnosing Word Recognition Difficulties

As the child reads the story, check any words in these lists which he doesn't recognize. If you don't wish to place check marks in your book, write the words on a separate piece of paper, then later rearrange them according to the headings given in the "Checking Aids." These groupings will indicate the types of phonic or word structure elements on which the pupil needs special practice.

PHONICS

INITIAL CONSONANTS

bags, bear, beast, before, began, best, better, big, bison, bone, both, bull, burned, but

carried, catch, cave, cavern, cold, come, corners, could, counsel, covered, cuds, cut

dark, days, deeply, dirt, doubt, down

faces, far, farther, feast, feet, few, find, fir, fire, fish, food, forward gallop, game, gasped, get, given, gone, good

had, hard, harm, have, heads, hear, heard, heart, help, hind, hold, home, horse, how, hundred, hungry, hunter

jump, just

kept, kill

laid, lamp, last, laugh, leaped, learning, leather, ledge, legs, let, lighted, like, lion, lived, long, look, loud, low, luck

made, magic, main, make, mammoths, may, meadow, means, meant, meat, men, might, moment, more, moss, mother, mouth, move, much

narrow, near, needed, needle, new, next, noise, none, now

paint, parents, people, perhaps, pictures, pierce, pig, point, poles, pouch, pulled

rain, really, red, repeated, ring, roasted, robe, rock, room

said, sang, sat, see, seldom, sewed, side, since, sing, sinew, sister, soft, some, son, song, southern, such, summer, suppose, surprise

tan, taste, tease, tell, tied, tight, time, together, told, too, tool, top, tucked

vision

wait, walk, walls, wandered, wanted, warm, wasted, went, were, wick, wild, will, wish, with, wolf, women, words, work, worry, would

years

FINAL CONSONANTS

shrub

magic

bad, bed, behind, broad, cloud, cold, end, find, food, forward, glad, good, had, hard, hind, hold, hundred, laid, need, old, red, said, spread, stood, told, toward, thread, upward, wild, word, would

chief, cliff, off, wolf

bag, pig

break, dark, look, took, walk, work

animal, bull, call, counsel, kill, shall, tell, until, will

alarm, arm, dream, from, harm, him, seldom, them, warm

an, began, bison, can, cavern, down, even, grown, lion, main, men, rain, ran, seen, skin, son, tan, then, vision, when, women

deep, gallop, help, jump, lamp, sharp, stop, top, up

after, bear, better, brother, clever, far, father, fir, for, hear, her, leather, mother, near, or, other, our, over, sharp, shelter, sister, Star, summer, supper, their, together, under, whisper

has, his, moss, this, unless, us, was

about, blanket, brought, but, chant, crept, dirt, doubt, eat, feast, fed, flint, front, get, great, interrupt, kept, left, let, meat, moment, next, not, paint, point, sat, set, shirt, short, that, thicket, thought, throat, tight, wait, went, what

CONSONANTS WITH TWO SOUNDS

Hard c: came, can, care, cliff, customs, magic

Soft c: faces, France, piece, place, scarce, twice

Hard g: forgotten, grease, hungry, nothing, shaggy, wriggled

Soft g: edge, huge, ledge, plunged, strange

INITIAL BLENDS

black, blankets

cleared, clever, cliff, climbing, cloud

flint

place, plains, plenty, plunged

sleepy, slope, slow, slipped

break, breaths, bring, broad, broke, brother, brought

crept

drawn, dream, drive

framework, France, friends, frightened, front

grass, grease, great, grown, grunted
pretended, protected
tribe, tried, true
scarce
skin
smooth
spirits, spoke
standing, Star, started, sticks, stomach, stone, stood, stop
twice
scrambled, scraped
strange, stripes, strips
shrub
spread
thread, threw, throat, through

MEDIAL BLENDS
scrambled, needle, wriggled, hundred, angry, hungry, surprise, custom

FINAL BLENDS
gasp, beast, feast, just

INITIAL SPEECH SOUNDS
chant, chasing, chunks
shall, sharp, she, shelter, shirt, short, should, shout
thank, thicket, thing, think, thought
then, there, this
what, when, while, whirled, whisper, white, why

MEDIAL SPEECH SOUNDS
singers, blankets, bushes, another, brother, father, mother

FINAL SPEECH SOUNDS
each, catch, much, pouch, which
enough, laugh

109

bush, fish, wish
attack, black, rock, stick, tuck
along, bring, long, ring, sing, song, thing
thank, think
both, breath, mammoth, mouth, sawtooth, with

VOWEL SOUNDS

Long a: amazed, ate, came, faces, game, made, make, scrape,
  shaded, strange, taste

Short a: added, and, animals, antelope, bags, black, chant,
  France, glad, had, lamp, mammoth, sat, shaggy, standing,
  than, thank, that, tan

Long e: even, he, pretended, she

Short e: best, better, clever, feel, get, help, kept, left, legs, let,
  men, next, shelter, then, went, when

Long i: bison, drive, fire, hind, knife, lighted, like, skin,
  stripe, times, tribe, while, white, wild

Short i: bring, cliff, fish, flint, him, kill, pig, sit, sister, skin,
  sticks, strips, thing, think, this, whisper, which, wick,
  will, wish, wriggling

Long o: bone, both, cold, hold, home, moment, no, old, only,
  over, poles, robe, slope, so, spoke, stone, told

Short o: got, not, on, rock, stop

Long u: huge, used

Short u: but, chunks, customs, cut, hundred, hungry, hunter,
  jump, just, luck, much, must, shrub, summer, upward

Long y: my

Short y: angry, hungry, plenty, shaggy, sunny, very, worry

ai: laid, main, paint, plains, rain, wait

ay: away, days, may, say

aw: draw, saw

ea: beast, cleared, dream, eat, feast, grease, hear, means, meat,
  near, really, repeat

ea: breath, dead, head, leather, meadow, ready, spread, thread

110

ea: break, great
ee: asleep, deeply, need, needle, see, seen, sleepy
ie: tied
ie: chief, piece
oa: oak, roasted, throat
oo: food, room, smooth, too, tool
oo: good, looked, stood, wood
oi: noise, point
oy: boy
ue: true
ew: chew, few, knew, new
ow: grown, show, slow, tomorrow
ow: brownish, how
ou: could, should, would
ou: enough, southern
ou: about, Cloud, counsel, found, loud, mouth, out, shouting
ou: brought, thought
Vowels followed by r: alarm, arm, dark, hard, harm, sharp, Star, start, upward, after, clever, interrupt, leather, over, shelter, sister, summer, supper, dirt, fir, first, girl, shirt, whirled
Vowels followed by l: almost, also, always, fall, talked, walk

Word Variants

COMPOUND WORDS

another, become, before, daybreak, everyday, framework, however, limestone, overhanging, passageway, sawtooth, sidewise, something, sometimes, therefore, tomorrow

HYPHENATED WORDS

oak-wood

INFLECTIONAL ENDINGS

added, admitted, amazed, answered, burned, carried, cleared,

111

covered, frightened, gasped, grunted, helped, killed, leaped, liked, lived, looked, needed, objected, painted, pictured, plunged, pretended, pulled, repeated, roasted, scrambled, scraped, sewed, sheltered, showed, slipped, started, striped, stopped, talked, thanked, threaded, tied, tucked, turned, used, waited, wandered, wanted, whirled, worked, wrapped, wriggled

clever, hunter, painter, singer

biggest

chanting, chasing, dreaming, eating, falling, galloping, hanging, hunting, learning, leaving, looking, pulling, putting, roasting, running, saying, shouting, singing, standing, stopping, taking, watching, waving

animals, bags, chunks, corners, cuds, customs, days, edges, enemies, friends, mammoths, paintings, parents, pictures, pieces, points, sides, skins, stripes, strips, words

PREFIXES

along, asleep

forward

uneven, unless

upward

SUFFIXES

eaten, forgotten, forgiven, sharpen

deeply, hardly, plainly, quickly, really, carefully

shaggy, sleepy, sunny

hopeful

brownish

southern

CONTRACTIONS

don't, we've

POSSESSIVES

bison's, Cloud's, girl's, Star's

NOTE

Reading TIA MARIA

In "Tia Maria," the next story, there are several Spanish words. These words should not be counted in the list of words that the child misses.

The teacher may help the pupil to pronounce these words: *Arturo* (ȧr tŏo′ rō), *Buenos Aires* (bwă′ nōs ī′ rās), *estancia* (ĕs tän′syä), *gaucho* (gou′ chō), *ombu* (ŏm′ bū), *Tia Maria* (tē′ ä mä rē′ ä).

THE VISIT
TO TIA MARIA

To Tia Maria's Ranch

Arturo and Berta lived with their father and mother in the beautiful city of Buenos Aires. Their home was in an apartment house on a narrow crooked street in the old part of the city. It is said that the Spanish people who founded Buenos Aires made its first streets very narrow so that people might ride or walk in the shade of the low buildings as much as possible during the hot summer days. Wide streets were not needed in those early days, for there were no trolley cars or buses and very few carriages. Almost everybody rode horseback.

In the old days, the horse was king in Argentina. People thought that nothing was too good for their horses. The saddles were made of leather with

114

patterns carved on them, and the mountings were of silver and sometimes of gold.

In the new part of Buenos Aires there are fine houses and straight, broad streets lined with trees. Parks made attractive by trees and flowers are found in many parts of the city.

Often Arturo and Berta rode horseback with their father in one of the great parks on the edge of the city. They liked Palermo Park best because there was a beautiful rose garden in it where thousands of roses were in blossom near a little lake.

While they rode over the smooth brick-red bridle path in the park, their father often told them stories of the time when he was a boy. He told them about his visits to his grandfather who lived in the country, far away on the Pampa.

"When you are on the Pampa," their father said, "you can ride as far and as fast as you like. There is nothing to stop you. As far as your eye can see there is nothing but prairie—hundreds of miles of it, almost as flat as a floor."

The stories which their father told them made Arturo and Berta long to go to the country and ride on the Pampa.

One day a letter came from Tia Maria inviting them to come to visit her on her estancia. Tia Maria is Spanish for Aunt Mary, and estancia is the Spanish word for ranch.

The letter made Arturo and Berta very happy.

But their mother said, "I am afraid that Berta is too young to go."

"Oh, I'm not too young!" cried Berta.

"I'll take care of her. I won't let anything happen to her," promised Arturo.

Arturo and Berta wanted very much to go to visit Tia Maria. At last their father and mother decided to let them take the trip.

From their home in Buenos Aires their father and mother took them, in the subway, to the railroad station.

When they reached the station platform, their mother opened her bag and took out two little packages. "Here is a gaucho handkerchief for each

of you, to wear around your neck when you ride on the Pampa. The red handkerchief is for Berta, and the purple one is for Arturo."

Soon the bell rang for the train to start. Arturo and Berta waved good-by from the car window. "Adios, adios!" they called.

"Adios, adios!" called their father and mother from the station platform.

All day and part of the night, the brother and sister traveled over the flat Pampa. At last the train came to the station where Tia Maria was to meet them. As the porter helped the two sleepy children off the train, they saw their aunt waiting for them.

"Tia Maria! Tia Maria!" they called out happily.

Arturo and Berta were so stiff from sitting still so long that they could hardly climb over the wheel to the high seat of Tia Maria's old-fashioned carriage. The cold night air made them shiver. The moonlight seemed almost as bright as day. Pulled by two lively horses, the carriage bounced them up and down as it rolled along the wide dirt road. Soon they were wide awake, and Tia Maria saw that their eyes, bright as the stars, danced with excitement. The full moon was high above their heads, and the dark ground seemed far below the high

seat of the carriage. They seemed to be swinging through the air.

The horses trotted so fast that in less than two hours they reached the estancia, which was ten miles from the railroad station.

It was past midnight when they went to bed in Tia Maria's great white house which was very much larger than their house in Buenos Aires. Near the house was a great spreading ombu tree.

118

On the Pampa

The next morning when Arturo and Berta came to breakfast, there was no one in the dining room. They helped themselves to the bread and butter and quince jam and milk which had been set out on the long, bare table.

After breakfast, they dressed in their riding clothes and tied the gaucho handkerchiefs around their necks. Tia Maria took them to the stable, which was built with an open veranda at the front.

It was much larger than any railroad station which they had passed on the Pampa. The arms of a tall windmill sang *clang-clang*, while pumping water for the cattle to drink.

"There are more than twenty horses in the stable," said Tia Maria. "You may each pick out a horse which you want to have for your own while you are here."

Arturo chose a black horse with two white hind feet. For a long time Berta could not decide which horse to pick out. Finally a brown horse with a white star on his forehead whinnied. She thought that meant that the horse wanted her to take him, and so she walked up to him, put her arms around his neck, and whispered, "You shall be my horse."

Every day Arturo and Berta went riding over the Pampa. Sometimes they rode alone. Sometimes Tia Maria or one of the gauchos rode with them. Gauchos are cowboys who take care of the cattle and the sheep on an estancia.

It was the lambing season. Young lambs were learning to stand on wobbly legs, and older ones were gamboling about. One day Arturo and Berta saw a lamb trying to stand on three legs. The poor little thing did not run away when they rode up to it, but bleated as if it wanted help.

120

Arturo got off his horse and stooped down to see what was the matter. "Its leg is broken," said he.

Berta's horse seemed to know that they were trying to help. It stood very still while Arturo was lifting the lamb up so that Berta could hold it on her saddle. Berta rode back to the stable holding the lamb as carefully as she could.

One of the gauchos set the lamb's leg and bandaged it with a splint.

"I'll give the lamb milk and take care of it until its leg is well," said the gaucho. "Then I'll take the splint off and put the lamb back with the flock."

On another day, Tia Maria rode with Berta and Arturo. At noon they were far from home. They ate boiled beef for dinner in a little thatched hut with an old gaucho and his wife. The man was too old to do much work, but he took care of the windmills and kept the troughs filled with water for the cattle.

A week later, after a heavy rain in the night, the pampas grass suddenly turned very green. Every day it grew taller and taller. Often Arturo and Berta rode through patches of pampas grass taller than they were, even when they were sitting on their horses.

One day Tia Maria said, "I am going to take the

121

train today to Buenos Aires, where I must attend to some business. I will stay in your house in Buenos Aires while you take care of my house."

Lost in the Tall Grass

The next day Arturo and Berta started off early in the morning for a ride on the Pampa.

"I'll race you!" called Arturo, galloping ahead.

Soon Berta got tired of racing and walked her horse. After a while, she saw an ostrich strutting along between the patches of tall grass. Berta turned her horse to follow the ostrich.

She followed the ugly long-legged bird, darting this way and that until she was hot and tired. She got off her horse near a clump of tall pampas grass to rest in the shade of it. Soon she was fast asleep.

Arturo had galloped on ahead, and it was a long time before he looked around and noticed that Berta was not following him. He saw her horse, but she was not in the saddle. He rode up to the horse, but Berta was nowhere to be seen. Arturo called, "Berta! Berta!"

The only answer was the whistling of the wind.

At last he decided to ride back to the stable. Berta's horse tried to follow, but Arturo drove the horse back. He hoped that Berta would find her horse and ride home.

Arturo could not find a gaucho in the stable. Then he went to the kitchen. Nobody was there but the cook, who was an old, old woman dozing by the open fire. He shook the old woman to wake her up, and called, "Berta is lost. What shall I do?"

"Ask the gauchos," she said, sleepily. "The gauchos will find her. Go eat your dinner. It's on the table in the dining room." The old woman went to sleep again.

Arturo went into the dining room, but he did not eat any dinner. Then again he went back to the stable. He could not find a gaucho, but he did see Berta's horse return by itself to the stable.

123

When Berta opened her eyes, she looked for Arturo and then for her horse. Her horse was nowhere to be seen, and neither was Arturo. She called, but there was no answer. She did not know how long she had been asleep. She thought that it must have been a long time because she was so hungry and thirsty.

Berta called "Arturo!" again and again. She could not call very loudly because her mouth was so dry.

She stood up and looked around, trying to remember which way she had come. All she saw was the sky and the great flat Pampa. She realized that she was lost.

"Oh, will anyone ever come to find me?" she sobbed. "But it won't do any good to cry."

She sat down on the ground again. The sun be-

gan to go down, and the wind to blow colder and colder. She was so cold that she got up and began to walk to keep herself warm.

It was almost dark when she heard the sound of an airplane in the distance. She could see the plane coming nearer and nearer. It had great silver wings.

"Oh, perhaps someone in the airplane will see me!" thought Berta. She took the red gaucho handkerchief from her neck, and standing on tiptoe waved it high above her head. Then she saw that it was coming down to land on the ground not far away, where there was no tall grass and the ground was hard.

Frantically she ran toward the great silver wings, waving her red handkerchief. "I'm lost! Take me home, please, I'm lost!" she begged.

When the plane landed, she heard a voice calling from it, "Berta! Berta!"

She knew the voice. "Tia Maria, are you really here?" she cried.

"Yes, I am here," said Tia Maria, who by this time was climbing out of the airplane.

Berta threw her arms around Tia Maria's neck. "How did you know that I was here? You are the most wonderful aunt in all the world to come and find me," she half sobbed and half laughed.

Tia Maria patted Berta's hand, and said, "Arturo telephoned me that you were lost. I rushed to the airport. There I found one of the pilots who is an old friend of mine. Last year he took me, in this same airplane, over my land so that I could count my cattle. I thought that if I could see my cattle from an airplane, I could also see my niece. I am not sure that I would have seen you so easily if you had not waved your red handkerchief."

"I have done a good deal of flying," said the pilot, smiling down at Berta, "but I have never before gone out to find a little girl."

"Climb into the airplane, Berta," said Tia Maria, "and our friend, the pilot, will take us home. Arturo is anxious to know that you are safe. He thought it was his fault that you were lost. We'll telephone your mother and father in Buenos Aires that you are safe. Everybody will be happy to know that you are not alone on the Pampa after dark."

"And I am happier than anybody," said Berta.

126

CHECKING AIDS FOR TEACHERS

LEVEL: Sixth Reader, latter part of book

The Visit to Tia Maria

COMPREHENSION CHECKS

Part I   To Tia Maria's Ranch
Pages 114–18, 765 words

LITERAL COMPREHENSION QUESTIONS

1   Where did Arturo and Berta live?
ANSWER: In Buenos Aires.

2   What explanation was given for the narrow streets in Buenos Aires?
ANSWER: It was said that the Spanish people who founded Buenos Aires made its first streets very narrow so that people might ride or walk in the shade of the low buildings as much as possible during the hot summer days.

3   Describe the new part of Buenos Aires.
ANSWER: In the new part of the city there are fine houses and straight, broad streets lined with trees; there are many attractive parks with trees and flowers.

4   Why did the children like Palermo Park the best?
    ANSWER: It had a beautiful rose garden near a little lake.

5   According to the father's description, what is a pampa?
    ANSWER: It is a large prairie flat as a floor.

6   What did the letter that the children received from Tia Maria say?
    ANSWER: It was an invitation from Tia Maria for the children to visit her.

7. What do the words *Tia Maria* and *estancia* mean?
    ANSWER: *Tia Maria* is Spanish for "Aunt Mary" and *estancia* is Spanish for "ranch."

8   What did Mother give the children before they left to visit Tia Maria?
    ANSWER: A gaucho handkerchief for each child to wear around the neck when riding.

9   What kind of weather did the children find on the night of their arrival?
    ANSWER: It was clear and cold.

10 How long did it take the horses to travel the ten miles from the railroad station to Tia Maria's home?
    ANSWER: It took two hours.

INTERPRETATION QUESTIONS

1   Why are wide streets needed now in Buenos Aires?
    ANSWER: Buenos Aires has buses, trolley cars, and automobiles now, as well as horses and wagons.

2   Why did the people of Argentina in the old days consider the horse as king?
    ANSWER: The horse was their only means of transportation in the city and over the vast pampas.

3   What is a bridle path? Why is it so called?

128

ANSWER: A bridle path is a path open only to people riding horses. It is probably so called because the only part of a harness which is on a riding horse is a bridle, or the headgear of the horse.

4 Why is Spanish spoken in Argentina?

ANSWER: It is spoken because Argentina was originally settled by the Spaniards.

5 What wheel was it that the children climbed over to get to the high seat on Tia Maria's carriage?

ANSWER: The back wheel of the carriage.

6 What clue does the story give you which indicates that Buenos Aires is a big city?

ANSWER: It has a subway to take people to different parts of the city.

7 For what reason did Mother give Arturo and Berta colored handkerchiefs to wear around their necks?

ANSWER: Probably to keep their necks from getting sunburned while riding on the Pampa.

8 How long would it have taken the children to travel from the railroad station to Tia Maria's home in an automobile, even at a slow speed of thirty miles per hour?

ANSWER: It would have taken twenty minutes. (Ten miles is $\frac{1}{3}$ of 30 miles; $\frac{1}{3}$ of 60 minutes is 20 minutes.)

9 Why did the children have the impression of swinging through the air while traveling out to Tia Maria's home?

ANSWER: The seat on the wagon was high and it bounced up and down as they traveled.

10 Do you think Tia Maria was wealthy? Why or why not?

ANSWER: She seemed wealthy for she had a great white house, a carriage with horses, and much land.

129

LITERAL COMPREHENSION QUESTIONS

1   What did the children have for breakfast at the estancia?
ANSWER: Bread and butter, quince jam, and milk.

2   How did the cattle on the Pampa get their drinking water?
ANSWER: It was pumped by a windmill.

3   Describe the horse that Arturo chose and the one that Berta selected.
ANSWER: Arturo chose a black horse with two white hind feet; Berta picked a brown horse with a white star on his forehead.

4   What made Berta decide on the brown horse?
ANSWER: The horse whinnied and she thought that meant that the horse wanted her to choose him.

5   What are gauchos?
ANSWER: Gauchos are cowboys who take care of the cattle and sheep on an estancia.

6   Why was the lamb bleating?
ANSWER: Its leg was broken.

7   How did Arturo show that he was a kind person?
ANSWER: He got off his horse, examined the lamb, saw that its leg was broken, and lifted it up onto Berta's saddle so that she could take it back to the stable.

8   What did the gaucho plan to do with the lamb?
ANSWER: He planned to take care of it until it was well, then put it back with the flock.

9   What work did the old man do?
ANSWER: He took care of the windmills and kept the troughs filled with water for the cattle.

10   What exchange did Tia Maria propose at the end of this section?

ANSWER: She said she would stay in the children's home in Buenos Aires while they could take care of her house.

INTERPRETATION QUESTIONS

1 Why were windmills necessary on the ranches near Tia Maria's home, while they are no longer used by dairy farmers in our country?

ANSWER: The pampas people evidently did not have electricity. Our present-day dairy farmers pump water into their barns by electricity.

2 Why were gauchos necessary on the Pampa?

ANSWER: They had to watch the cattle and sheep to keep them from straying away over the vast miles of pampas land.

3 What do you think the cattle and lambs had for food?

ANSWER: They ate pampas grass.

4 Why did the old man live in a thatched hut?

ANSWER: Wood was not available on the Pampa, and brick and cement were too expensive for the old man, so he probably thatched a hut with pampas grass.

5 The latter part of this section of the story tells you that the pampas grass had grown so high in patches that it was taller than Arturo and Berta, even when they were sitting on their horses. Does this give you any hint as to what may happen next? If so, what?

ANSWER: Yes. The children may get lost.

Part III   Lost in the Tall Grass
Pages 122–26, 850 words

LITERAL COMPREHENSION QUESTIONS

1 How did Berta happen to get lost?

ANSWER: She followed an ostrich off over the Pampa.

2 Why didn't Arturo realize that Berta was not following him?

ANSWER: He had galloped ahead and it was a long time before he looked around and noticed that Berta was not following him.

3 Arturo did not let Berta's horse follow him. Why?

ANSWER: He hoped that Berta would find her horse and ride home.

4 What difficulty did Arturo have when he got back to the stable?

ANSWER: He couldn't find a gaucho to go out and look for Berta.

5 What made Berta think she had been asleep a long time?

ANSWER: She was so hungry and thirsty.

6 Why did Berta become especially uncomfortable as time went by?

ANSWER: The wind become colder and colder.

7 How did Berta signal the airplane?

ANSWER: She waved her gaucho handkerchief.

8 How did Tia Maria learn that Berta was lost?

ANSWER: Arturo telephoned to her.

9 How did Tia Maria happen to know the pilot?

ANSWER: He had taken her over her land last year to count her cattle.

10 Who had to be informed that Berta was safe?

ANSWER: Arturo and her father and mother.

INTERPRETATION QUESTIONS

1 Do you think Arturo's decision to ride back to the stable without Berta was a wise one? Why or why not?

ANSWER: Yes. He hoped to find gauchos at the stable who would aid him in finding Berta.

2   If Berta had not lost her horse, might things have been different? How?

ANSWER: The horse might have found his way back to the stable and taken Berta with him.

3   Why couldn't Arturo find any gauchos to help him look for Berta?

ANSWER: They were in different parts of the Pampa herding their cattle and sheep.

4   Why did the old woman seem to be more concerned about having Arturo eat his dinner than she was about Berta being lost?

ANSWER: She was so old that she had lost interest in responsibilities other than her own, which was cooking meals for people to eat.

5   Why didn't Arturo eat any dinner?

ANSWER: He was much too worried about Berta.

6   How could Berta have figured out approximately how long she had slept?

ANSWER: She could have figured the time from the changing position of the sun. When she first fell asleep, the sun was high in the sky, and when she awoke, the sun was going down. From noon until sundown in the summer might have been eight or nine hours.

7   What evidence have you that Arturo was a resourceful boy?

ANSWER: When he couldn't find any gauchos to help him, he telephoned to Buenos Aires thinking that his aunt would know what to do.

8   Is there any evidence in this part of the story that showed Berta also was resourceful?

ANSWER: Yes. She took off her red gaucho handkerchief and used it to signal the pilot.

9   Why did Arturo think it was his fault that Berta was lost?

133

ANSWER: He had promised his parents that he would take care of Berta.

10 Why was it necessary for Tia Maria to employ an airplane in order to count her cattle?

ANSWER: The cattle were scattered all over the Pampa amidst the tall grass; not all of them could be seen by a person riding on horseback.

VOCABULARY CHECKS

Organized for Use in Diagnosing Word Recognition Difficulties

As the child reads the story, check any words in these lists which he doesn't recognize. If you don't wish to place check marks in your book, write the words on a separate piece of paper, then later rearrange them according to the headings given in the "Checking Aids." These groupings will indicate the types of phonic and word structure elements on which the pupil needs special practice.

See note on page 113 about the Spanish words in this selection.

PHONICS

INITIAL CONSONANTS

back, bag, bandaged, bare, beautiful, bed, beef, before, bell, below, Berta, best, between, bird, boiled, bounced, boy, Buenos, building, buses, business, butter

came, car, care, carriage, carved, cattle, cold, come, cook, could, country

danced, dark, darting, distance, done, down, dozing, during

far, fast, father, fault, feet, few, finally, find, fine, filled fire, first, follow, found, full

galloping, gamboling, garden, gaucho, girl, give, gold, good

happen, happy, heads, heavy, help, here, high, hind, home,
 horse, hot, hours, house, how, hundred, hungry, hut
jam
kept, king, kitchen
lake, lamb, learning, leather, legs, less, let, letter, liked, lived,
 little, long, low
made, many, Maria, matter, meant, meet, miles, milk, might,
 moon, morning, mother, mountings, mouth, much, must
narrow, near, neck, needed, neither, never, new, next, niece,
 night, noon, noticed
packages, Palermo, Pampa, parks, part, patches, patch, patted,
 patterns, people, perhaps, pick, pilots, poor, porter,
 possible, pumping, purple, put
race, rain, ranch, range, reach, realizes, really, remember, red,
 rest, return, ride, road, rode, rolled, room, rose. rushed
saddle, safe, said, same, seat, seen, set, silver, soon, sound,
 subway, suddenly, sun
table, take, tall, telephone, ten, Tia, time, tired, told, took,
 turn
veranda, very, visit, voice
wake, walked, wanted, we, went, wobbly, woman, work
year, yes, you, young

FINAL CONSONANTS

afraid, ahead, and, around, attend, bed, bread, broad, bird,
 cold, could, crooked, did, found, friend, gold, good, had,
 hard, heard, hind, hold, land, old, red, road, said, stand,
 stood, told, wind
beef, half, if, off, stiff
bag, dining, during, leg, morning
dark, milk, took, walk, week, work
all, bell, full, girl, still, until, well, wheel, will
am, blossom, from, him, jam, platform, room, warm
an, been, between, brown, can, children, down, garden, hap-

135

pen, in, man, moon, often, on, open, own, return, run, season, seen, soon, station, sun, ten, than, train, when

asleep, clump, help, keep, stop, trip, up

after, air, another, answer, butter, car, dinner, far, father, for, floor, leather, letter, mother, near, neither, never, over, poor, porter, remember, shiver, silver, star, summer, their, water, wear, your

adios, as, Buenos Aires, his, less, this

about, apartment, aunt, bright, built, but, dirt, excitement, feet, flat, front, great, high, hot, hut, it, kept, let, meet, might, next, night, not, part, pilot, seat, set, splint, straight, street, that, thought, visit, want, went

CONSONANTS WITH TWO OR MORE SOUNDS

Hard c: because	*s:* sister
Soft c: city	*s(sh):* sure
Hard g: begged, hungry	*s(z):* was
Soft g: bandaged, edge	

INITIAL BLENDS

black, bleated, blossom, blow

clang, climb, clothes, clump

flat, flock, floor, flowers, flying

plane, platform, please

sleep

bread, breakfast, bridle, bright, broad, broken, brother, brown

crooked, cry

dry

frantically, friend, from, front

grass, great, green, grew, ground

prairie, promised

train, tree, trip, trolley, trotted, troughs

smiling

Spanish

stable, stand, stars, start, station, stay, stiff, still, stood, stooped, stop, stories

twenty, two

swinging

spreading

straight, street, strutting

splint

three, threw, through

MEDIAL BLENDS

stable, table

bridle, saddle

airplane, purple

asleep

hungry

country

whispered

distance, ostrich, thirsty

FINAL BLENDS

ask

almost, breakfast, fast, first, last, lost, most, must, past, rest

INITIAL SPEECH SOUNDS

chose

quince

shade, shall, she, sheep, shiver, shook

that, them, then, their, there, they, this

thatched, thirsty, thought, threw

what, when, where, which, while, whinnied, whispered, whistling, white

who

MEDIAL SPEECH SOUNDS

handkerchief, gaucho, kitchen, patches, thatched

laughed

telephone

rushed

brother, clothes, father, leather, mother, neither, nothing

nowhere

each, much, ostrich, ranch, reach, which
trough
Spanish
back, brick, neck, pick
clang, king, long, morning, nothing, rang, sang, young
drink
mouth, path, with

VOWELS

Long a: came, later, made, plane, racing, safe, shade, stable, station, table, take, waved

Short a: bag, black, can, cattle, flat, happy, jam, land, man, matter, Pampa, patches, pattern, ranch, saddle, Spanish, stand, than, that, thatched

Long e: me, she

Short e: bed, Berta, best, dressed, edge, help, leg, less, let, letter, neck, next, never, rest, telephoned, them, themselves, well, went, when

Long i: bridle, bright, climb, dining, find, finally, fine, high, hind, lined, miles, night, ride, time, while, white, wide, wife

Short i: brick, children, did, dinner, give, king, kitchen, little, lived, milk, pick, shiver, silver, sitting, splint, stiff, still, thing, trip, visit, whinnied, whistling, will, wind, window, wings, with

Long o: alone, broken, chose, cold, dozing, go, gold, home, most, old, only, open, over, rode, so, those, told, trotted

Short o: not, on, stop, wobbly

Long u: ombu

Short u: buses, but, butter, clump, hundreds, hungry, hut, much, run, rushed, subway, sun, strutting, until, up

Long y: cry, dry, sky, trying

Short y: city, happy, heavy, suddenly, trolley

138

ai: afraid, railroad, rain, straight, train, waiting

ay: days, may, stay, way

au: because, fault

aw: saw

ea: bleated, each, easily, eat, deal, please, reached, really, seat

ea: ahead, breakfast, heavy, leather, meant, spreading, wear

ee: beef, feet, meet, needed, seen, sheep, sleep, street, three, tree, wheel

ei: neither

ie: tied, tried

ie: niece

oe: tiptoe

oo: moon, noon, smooth, too

oo: cook, crooked, good, looked, shook, stood, took

oi: boiled, voice

oy: boy

ew: few, new, threw

ow: below, blow, follow, know, low, narrow, own, window

ow: brown, down, flowers, how

ou: about, around, bounced, count, found, ground, house, loudly, mountings, mouth, sound, thousands

ou: thought, troughs

ou: country

ou: through

Vowels followed by r: are, Argentina, arms, Arturo, car, carved, dark, darting, far, hardly, larger, Maria, parks, Berta, her, veranda, were, dirt, first, girl, thirsty, for, horse, more, morning, platform, porter, purple, turned

Vowels followed by l or w: all, almost, called, tall, walk, saw

WORD VARIANTS

COMPOUND WORDS

airplane, airport, anybody, anyone, breakfast, cowboys,

everybody, grandmother, handkerchief, horseback, itself, midnight, moonlight, nobody, nowhere, railroad, someone, sometimes, themselves, tiptoe, windmill

brick-red, good-by, long-legged, old-fashioned

bandaged, begged, boiled, bounced, bleated, called, carved, crooked, decided, dressed, filled, founded, galloped, helped, landed, laughed, liked, lined, lived, needed, noticed, opened, passed, patted, pulled, reached, realized, rolled, rushed, seemed, sobbed, started, stooped, telephoned, thatched, tied, tired, traveled, trotted, walked, wanted, whinnied, whispered

colder, happier, larger, nearer, older, taller

calling, climbing, coming, darting, dozing, flying, following, galloping, gamboling, holding, inviting, lambing, learning, lifting, pumping, racing, riding, sitting, spreading, standing, strutting, swinging, waiting, waving, whistling

arms, buildings, buses, carriages, cars, clothes, days, flowers, gauchos, handkerchiefs, heads, horses, hours, houses, hundreds, lambs, legs, miles, necks, ones, packages, pampas, parks, parts, patches, patterns, pilots, roses, saddles, stories, streets, thousands, trees, troughs, visits, wings

carefully, easily, finally, frantically, happily, hardly, lively, loudly, sleepily, suddenly, wobbly

hungry, sleepy, thirsty

apartment, excitement

beautiful, wonderful

attractive

Spanish

ahead, alone, apartment, asleep

below, excitement, forehead, midnight, return, subway, toward